Financial Management
for Contractors

For Hannah and John

Financial Management for Contractors

ALAN UPSON ARICS

BSP PROFESSIONAL BOOKS

OXFORD LONDON EDINBURGH
BOSTON PALO ALTO MELBOURNE

First published 1987

British Library
Cataloguing in Publication Data

Upson, Alan
  Financial management for contractors.
  1 Construction industry—Great Britain
  —Finance 2. Contractors' operations
  —Great Britain
  I. Title
  624   HD9715.G72
ISBN 0-632-01855-0

BSP Professional Books
Editorial Offices:
Osney Mead, Oxford OX2 OEL
  (*Orders*: Tel. 0865 240201)
8 John Street, London WC1N 2ES
23 Ainslie Place, Edinburgh EH3 6AJ
52 Beacon Street, Boston
  Massachusetts 02108, USA
667 Lytton Avenue, Palo Alto
  California 94301, USA
107 Barry Street, Carlton
  Victoria 3053, Australia

Set by V & M Graphics Ltd, Aylesbury, Bucks
Printed and bound in Great Britain

Acknowledgements
Figures from the Inland Revenue Booklet IR 14/15 (1982) reproduced
with the permission of the Controller of Her Majesty's Stationery
Office.

Extracts from ED40 and SSAP 9 reproduced by permission of The
Accounting Standards Committee.

Figure 5 reproduced by permission of The National Westminster
Bank.

Contents

Preface

Building contractors and developers are faced with innumerable problems in their day-to-day work in the construction industry. Losses, and possible ultimate financial failure, are an ever-present problem, and even the most successful contractors may operate on a very low percentage profit on turnover.

This book has therefore been written to identify many of the areas where builders are at risk and to set out, in a straightforward and easily understood manner, good business practice.

Particular emphasis has been placed on the interface between the builder's technical staff and the accountancy profession when dealing with the problems of valuing work in progress. The accounts, for example, of a shoe manufacturer will need careful appraisal when considering the value of stock of raw materials and stocks of the finished product, particularly if they are out of fashion. However, work in progress on the factory floor will be unlikely to extend for longer than one day.

On the other hand, in complete contrast, the valuation of work in progress for a building firm is all important, particularly where it will last for many months or even years. How work in progress should be valued, the associated levels of profit or loss, and how these should be accounted for, are all crucial ingredients of the financial accounts of a company. All too often, by legitimate manipulation of overheads, attributable profits and foreseeable losses, contractors can create a policy regarding profit taking which is extremely flexible. Such policies, sometimes known as 'creative accounting', produce widely different results in the financial accounts. Moreover, it is difficult to identify those contractors who have opted for cautious and prudent results, those who have rashly over-declared profits or mitigated losses, and those who lack the expertise to produce accounts or meaningful results. I have attempted to explain the strengths, weaknesses and dangers of such manipulation in the text.

The building industry in the UK is complex and comprises a variety of firms of very differing sizes, ranging from one-man operations to major public companies. This book has been aimed primarily at the management of small to medium sized companies, employing from five to fifty office staff. This does not mean that the proprietor of a very small building company, or indeed the middle management of national contractors, might not equally be helped to a greater understanding of the various aspects of financial management on profitability and financial control.

Accountants who are involved in construction activities, either within a company or as auditors, may also gain an insight into some of the complexities of valuation of work in progress from the viewpoint of construction management.

The terms 'contractor', 'builder', 'master-builder', 'building contractor', 'developer', or a combination of such titles are used to describe a variety of construction companies in the UK. The company envisaged when writing the book would be engaged in small works, contracting and residential development, hence the introduction of the chapter on land purchase. I have therefore used the more general term 'builder' in the text, unless specific reference was required to contracting.

Equally, for simplicity, JCT 80 (Private Edition) has been used throughout when referring to contract terms and conditions.

Finally my thanks are due to Peter Hibberd of Bristol Polytechnic for reading the draft manuscript, and to John Campbell of Vale and West, Chartered Accountants, Reading, for reading through those chapters on accountancy. Special thanks are due to my wife, Irene, for patience and perseverance during the many hours spent in discussion and typing.

Alan Upson
May 1987

1 Organisation and Structure of Construction Companies

INTRODUCTION

Perhaps no topic is more difficult to consider than the organisation and structure of construction companies but this is an essential factor in the financial stability of any firm. Builders when contemplating their management structure are faced with three basic problems:

- getting work
- getting work executed and completed to time, of the right quality and to cost
- getting work paid for

Each company meets these challenges in its own way and the strengths developed by one are often the weaknesses in another.

There are over 67 000 general builders in Great Britain and approximately 1000 go into compulsory or voluntary liquidation each year. Over a ten-year period liquidations in the construction industry have accounted for between 13% and 18% of all liquidations. Because of the nature of the building industry, if a company fails it is usually only money that is lost. The basic resources of a skilled labour force, plant and administrative expertise are dissipated to other companies with little or no disruption to the industry as a whole. This is of course in direct contrast to manufacturing industry where, once the investment in fixed plant and productive capacity is lost, it is often gone for ever. On the other hand some manufacturing companies, having gone into liquidation or receivership, are sold for low figures, thus enabling the business to continue in different ownership with a reduced capital base and so providing an opportunity for them to become more competitive.

It is perhaps worth noting that of approximately 67 000 firms of general builders, 62 000 employ less than 13 men, which represents one third of the labour employed in the industry. Small firms employing less than 10 men are responsible for approximately 25% of the construction work in the UK. Firms employing between 10 and 50 men undertake a further 25%, and 75% of the value of construction work is completed by firms employing less than 100 men.

The most helpful way of analysing the structure of construction companies is perhaps to examine the patterns and pressures caused by growth. Each stage in this development process can then be discussed in detail, starting with the very small builder and progressing to the national contractor.

THE VERY SMALL BUILDER

A few construction companies may commence operations with a large injection of capital and expertise and avoid the rigours of the early growth process. The majority of builders, however – including many of the well-known national names – were very small at their inception; one man on his own or with a mate is the norm. Over 75% of all general builders employ less than five operatives.

Many very small builders commence operations when a craftsman with a trade background, possibly after operating for a while as a labour-only sub-contractor, decides to quote for small extensions, alterations or maintenance work. The craftsman will of course use his own expertise, such as carpentry or bricklaying, and by acquiring skills in other trades do as much work as possible himself. When this proves impossible other sub-contractors will be employed to undertake those aspects of the work which are beyond his expertise or capacity.

Such very small enterprises, with high levels of entrepreneurial thrust, are often very successful, providing work of excellent quality and a personal service to clients. Frequently sole proprietors or partnerships prefer to maintain a steady turnover and 'go it alone' without the added responsibility and problems that arise with expansion. The success of the enterprise obviously depends on the working proprietor and sometimes the administrative back-up is weak, with estimating and book-work being undertaken at evenings or weekends. A wife or other member of the family with secretarial or accounting skills is an obvious advantage.

Generally very small builders are good at getting work done, but may lack the surveying knowledge to ensure that estimates are realistic, or the costing expertise to render accurate accounts to clients and ensure payment for work.

Very small firms are often vulnerable because they operate on a low level of invested capital or with only a small overdraft facility. If a client is slow to pay, or indeed fails to pay, they may not therefore have the financial resources to continue trading. One solution used by some enterprises is to quote a figure for small works which is double the estimated cost and either ask for a 50% deposit in advance or stage payments early in the project programme. In any event it is not easy for the builder to investigate the financial standing of the client and most contracts are undertaken on the basis of mutual trust.

Because of the pressure of circumstances it is common practice for many very small builders to fail to obtain quotations for materials or to be forced to collect materials direct from the local builders' merchant, often at enhanced rates.

One advantage over larger firms is that where a builder has under-priced a job, the proprietor will resolve the problem by working longer hours or accepting a reduced income for a short period, thus mitigating the potential loss. The accounts will show the success, or lack of it, of the enterprise overall, although they will probably only be prepared by the accountant on an annual basis and will not show profit or loss on individual projects.

By contrast some very small enterprises are started by other members of the construction team, such as contract managers, surveyors or accountants who use their administrative expertise to obtain work and secure payment, but use labour-only or labour and material sub-contractors to get the actual work done. The success of such an approach will of course be heavily dependent on the ability and quality of the site labour used. Moreover, there will often be difficulty in acquiring sub-contractors prepared to undertake small projects, at the right time, at the right price and of the right quality, thus creating problems of continuity.

In the case of most alteration or extension work, the client will be permanently on site and this can, from a management viewpoint, be very demanding. Notwithstanding this, very small builders often achieve a high quality output with a personal service to the client and with a turnover of between £20 000 and £40 000 per annum.

SMALL BUILDERS

A percentage of very small builders will expand their enterprise and, if they have not already done so, most will trade as a limited liability company.

SOLE TRADER

As a sole trader the owner of a business has extensive freedom and there are no legal formalities or obligations to produce audited accounts, except for the Inland Revenue. The owner is, of course, personally liable for all business debts.

PARTNERSHIP

A business trading as a partnership will be jointly owned by two or more people. Although a verbal agreement is often used, it is preferable to have a formal partnership agreement, drafted by a solicitor, in order to avoid possible future disputes over such issues as the share of business owned by each partner, capital formation, division of profits and termination of the agreement. If a partner dies it may be necessary to sell off assets to meet a tax liability. Each partner is of course personally liable for the total debts of the enterprise.

There can be an advantage, in a period of initial expansion, in having a sleeping partner who does not take part in the day-to-day running of the business, but provides capital in exchange for a share of the profits.

It will be apparent from the above comments that those contemplating entering into partnership together must do so on the basis of mutual trust and, wherever possible, matched abilities or personal contribution.

LIMITED COMPANY

Limited liability companies are subject to the provisions of the Companies Acts 1948 to 1985. The company exists independently of its founders or directors and there is no personal liability for debts, although the bank will usually require a personal guarantee if extensive borrowing is required.

The company must have at least one director and a company secretary. The founders may own shares in the company and can be employed as directors. Capital can of course be raised by issuing shares in the company.

Company accounts must be audited annually by a qualified accountant and certain information is available to the general public. Trading cannot commence until various documents, including the memorandum and articles of association, are lodged with the registrar of companies and a certificate of incorporation has been obtained.

It is possible to buy a company 'off the shelf' through a solicitor or accountant from firms specialising in company formation, at a cost of around £100–nearer £200 if the name is to be changed. It is not essential, but may be preferable to change the name of the company, and before a specific name is chosen it is useful to obtain a copy of *Business names – Guidance Notes*, published by the Department of Trade.

If the turnover of the company exceeds (currently) £7000 a quarter it will be necessary to register for VAT. Full details are available from HM Customs and Excise.

In looking at the expansion of a typical building business, it would perhaps be helpful to examine the possible structure at two stages – when employing up to 10 men and when employing up to 50 men.

STAGE ONE

Over the years, the very small builder is likely to gather around him a useful group of operatives either directly employed or, more probably, labour-only or labour and material sub-contractors, semi-permanently retained, such as ground workers, bricklayers, carpenters, roof tilers, plasterers, plumbers and electricians. The advantages and disadvantages of the use of directly employed labour or labour-only sub-contractors are discussed in detail in Chapter 6, although with the small building company there are obvious financial and administrative advantages in the use of sub-contractors.

A small building company employing up to 10 men will often continue with a working proprietor. The working proprietor will usually divide his time between obtaining work and getting work done and will probably continue to work in his own trade as well as supervising the work of others.

The more enterprising may have retained a part-time bookkeeper, estimator/surveyor or accountant to assist with administration, and often a retired person with a lifetime's expertise in one or more of these areas can be invaluable.

When the proprietor takes upon himself the responsibility for administration, including both estimating and bookkeeping, his ability (or indeed lack of it) will almost certainly have a dramatic impact on the success of the enterprise at this point in its growth.

It is possible that a primitive costing system may have been introduced and as a result the once- or twice-a-year assessment of progress by the acountant/auditor may provide the proprietor with management accounting information, including some indication of the profit or loss on individual projects.

Many companies, even at this early stage, decide to undertake some form of speculative development, provided sufficient capital can be obtained from the bank or generated internally. Although financial returns from development can be greater than those realised from contracting, the risks are extensive, particularly when market conditions are deteriorating and interest rates rising. In Chapter 2 when discussing cash flow, the marked contrast between the capital required to undertake development and that required for contracts is discussed in detail.

The basic division between speculative development on the one hand and contracts on the other is extensive. With development work there is a much greater likelihood of profit, and also a freedom from the constraints imposed by clients and architects. In addition the builder may have greater control over programming, workload, specification and construction methods. Some companies continue to expand both their development and contracting operations while others concentrate on one or the other. With companies of this size the proprietor may well be able to meet the varying requirements of both contracts and development, but in larger organisations some degree of specialisation will be essential. At site level, for example, the foreman of a development site must be adept at handling individual purchasers and have a good 'bedside manner', while on contracts, on the other hand, he will be faced with meeting the demands of an architect and clerk of works.

The turnover of a company at this stage in its development is likely to be in the region of £200000 per annum and will include a variety of projects such as small works, extensions, individual houses under contract, contracts up to, say, £50000 and possibly speculative development.

Where the proprietor is intelligent and efficient, and has management expertise and the ability to provide a personal service to clients, the company may well be very profitable with potential for further expansion, particularly when the profits have been ploughed back into the business.

STAGE TWO

As a building firm expands, the next key stage is when the office staff have reached five in number with up to 50 men employed on the site, either directly or as labour-only and labour and material sub-contractors.

With this size of company the proprietor will normally be non-manual working and his background and abilities will be an important ingredient to success. Management ability is vital in an expanding company and a practical knowledge of construction, combined with an understanding of financial management, is essential. In larger companies it will be possible to buy in expertise but normally the proprietor in a small company will be the team leader.

Building businesses have been started and successfully expanded to this stage by proprietors from almost all trade and office backgrounds. It is difficult to make a valid judgement as to which background is most likely to provide the foundation for successful management and expansion, but in the author's experience those who started as carpenters and joiners, surveyors or contract managers, seem to be most successful.

One factor which can cause difficulties in small and medium-sized private companies is the conflict which may arise between family interests and the ability, expertise and loyalty of senior staff. There is often a tendency to promote members of the proprietor's family, irrespective of age or ability, over loyal and able members of staff, with possible resultant bad feeling and ultimately the loss of the staff concerned. Similarly, the proprietor may be reluctant to promote staff to director level, thus blocking possibilities for advancement.

The proprietors of many small businesses are often faced with the difficult task of integrating their own children or sons-in-law directly into the company without disruption. It will be necessary to make unbiased and valid judgements as to the ability of the family members concerned. One effective method is to arrange for the training and technical education of family members in another company and only attempt integration when they are fully mature. This will have the added advantage of the introduction of new concepts and ideas to the business.

Of the five staff working in the office a variety of combinations of expertise may develop and will obviously vary from company to company. A typical arrangement would be the proprietor as team leader, an accountant, a construction or contract manager, an estimator/ surveyor, and a telephonist/typist/admin. assistant. As this very small group will normally work together as a team, sharing the workload, personalities are very important. The estimator/surveyor will have wide responsibilities, probably including buying, and there may well be a conflict between estimating and other duties. The proprietor should have experience in all areas and therefore be able to offer assistance where it is most needed.

At this stage costing will be essential but it may not be integrated with the financial accounts and is unlikely to be regularly related to valuations other than at the end of the firm's financial year.

A building company of this size will almost certainly be trading as a limited company but the proprietors and directors may well be required to provide personal guarantees against any bank borrowing.

The type of projects comprising the company's annual turnover are likely to include contracts above £100 000 in value for private clients or local authorities and possibly the construction of small private developments. Such companies may also have a limited investment in their own plant, including scaffolding, lorries and concrete mixers.

A company at this stage in its growth is poised to enter perhaps the most competitive and challenging area of building operations – that of the medium-sized contractor/developer.

MEDIUM-SIZED CONTRACTORS/DEVELOPERS

At this next point of progress in the expansion of building business a number of subtle changes will take place. The term 'contractor', 'building contractor' or 'development company' may well have supplanted the perhaps less inspiring title of 'builder'. The number of office or administrative staff will have expanded to some 10 to 25, with a corresponding growth in the external labour force. The proprietor will normally have surrounded himself with a support group of key personnel at senior management or director level. The business may therefore be less dependent on the technical or financial management expertise of the proprietor, and more on his general management ability and personality. The proprietor or managing director must:

(a) Have a competent mind and the ability to generate confidence. It is essential for safe expansion to develop a good sense of judgement. It has been said that every man in the promotional ladder struggles to reach his level of incompetence.
(b) Have the ability to innovate new concepts, deal with many problems at the same time and maintain a high level of personal thrust, drive and output.
(c) Have the natural ability to inspire loyalty, and be adept at handling other members of the staff; to know when to rebuke and encourage in a way that ensures that the work gets done.
(d) Be able to delegate effectively by giving other people the authority to make decisions within defined limits. To this end responsibility for each job should be understood, agreed and clearly defined, preferably in writing.

(e) Keep lines of communication short by minimising the levels of authority. It should always be borne in mind, however that:
- no man can effectively serve two masters
- staff reporting to one man should be as equal in status as possible
- the number of staff reporting to one man should not normally exceed five or six

At this stage in the growth of a building company some degree of specialisation will usually have occurred. To some extent the type of work undertaken, such as small works, private contracts, contracts for local authorities or central government, design and build or package-deal contracts, and residential, commercial or industrial development, will govern the nature of staff and their structure and interrelationships.

The first management function to be specialised will almost certainly be the accounts, and of say 25 staff, five will be engaged with the financial and cost accounts, including probably a company secretary, chief accountant, cost clerk, sales and bought ledger clerk and a clerical assistant. A company of this size should have integrated cost and financial account (see Chapter 9), and a reasonably accurate cost value reconciliation procedure for the assessment of valuation of work in progress in the financial accounts.

The second most common area of specialisation will be estimating. When the company is tendering for work mainly on the traditional basis with bills of quantities provided by the client, only one estimator, with an assistant, will be required. On the other hand, where the company is engaged in development, design and build or package-deal contracts, either the estimating department may be expanded to include a design and taking-off section, or outside professionals will be employed. With small works, however, the estimator will probably also undertake the surveying function.

Staff in other specialised areas such as reception and typing, plant, transport and stores supervisors may be more effectively used if serving the whole company rather than a particular group or department.

The remaining key staff engaged in getting work done and paid for, including contract managers and surveyors, in some companies work in management teams and in others are departmentalised.

Management teams of a contract manager and surveyor, together with possible assistance from a technician helping with buying and planning, can be very effective. Company expansion progresses by increasing the number of teams and sharing the work between them. One team, for example, could be engaged in small works, one team in development, another in design and build and package-deal, and several in contracting.

There are obvious advantages to operating in this way, particularly with the potential for developing team spirit, detailed knowledge of all that is happening on site and very short lines of communication. In essence national contractors expand this concept when, on large contracts, the administrative and technical staff are all site-based, with only the estimating, accounts and costing functions being administered by head office.

The alternative management form of total departmentalisation is discussed in the next section.

LARGE CONTRACTORS/DEVELOPERS

Under this arbitrary definition should be included all provincial and individual companies with a turnover in excess of £5 or £6 million per annum. The office and administrative staff will have expanded to reach a figure of, say, between 50 and 75, with a corresponding level of site labour. To a large extent this book is aimed at companies of this size, and individual chapters deal with many aspects of their financial administration. For the majority of construction companies this may well be the maximum point of growth and in fact in fluctuating market conditions it may be difficult to maintain turnover from year to year. As a result staff will nearly always be under pressure because, for survival, overheads must be kept in check in relation to the corresponding annual turnover.

As previously stated, companies may specialise in contracting, development or design and build or package-deal contracts and maintain separate departments, divisions or subsidiary companies to deal with a variety of aspects of the construction industry.

There may well be arguments in favour of concentrating resources in one specialist area, but on balance, in the author's view, the concept of putting all eggs in one basket is perhaps unwise. This should be emphasised for a variety of reasons, for example, the contracting division may well generate cash flow to fund development. The author is aware that many companies 'front-end load' their contracts to generate surplus cash flow of many millions to this end. Equally, market conditions may be deteriorating in one sector while improving in another.

As the company expands, however, there are sound reasons for isolating certain aspects, say, residential development, either into a clearly defined department or as a separate company. With a company of this size the earlier concept of team management will be difficult to maintain unless large individual projects are entirely administered from the site. There will for a variety of reasons be a tendency for separate departments to be formed:

- It will be difficult to obtain staff of the calibre and all-round ability to function in a small team and some team members, therefore, may be weak links. Departments, on the other hand, can utilise staff of varying ability under supervision.
- If a team member is ill or resigns for any reason it may be more difficult to arrange cover for his duties and responsibilities.
- Departmentalisation may be more efficient by providing economies of scale and reducing duplication of effort. With buying, for example, a separate department will invariably obtain a better service and price than individual team members where the company's purchasing power has been dissipated.
- Greater specialisation may increase efficiency. For example, the surveyor in a small team may be responsible for buying, measurement of sub-contractors, interim valuations and the final account. Invariably, because of pressure of circumstances, the final account will be neglected.

A typical departmental management structure is shown in Fig. 1.1, which attempts to identify the various departments and their interrelationships.

Once a company is departmentalised it is essential to have a strong management team at director level to ensure that friction between staff does not develop and that all activities of the company are efficiently and effectively co-ordinated.

There is an obvious point of conflict between estimating (estimated cost) and contract management/surveying (actual cost). Furthermore, contract management is concerned to get work done to time, quality and cost. These factors are not necessarily related and individual contract managers concentrate on only one, or at best only two. But the surveying and accounts department will almost certainly emphasise cost, thus creating another possible point of conflict.

As the company expands, management of personnel becomes an increasingly important aspect of the day-to-day running of the business and great care must be taken if one wishes to get the best out of staff.

Individual members of staff will be motivated by many different factors, such as:

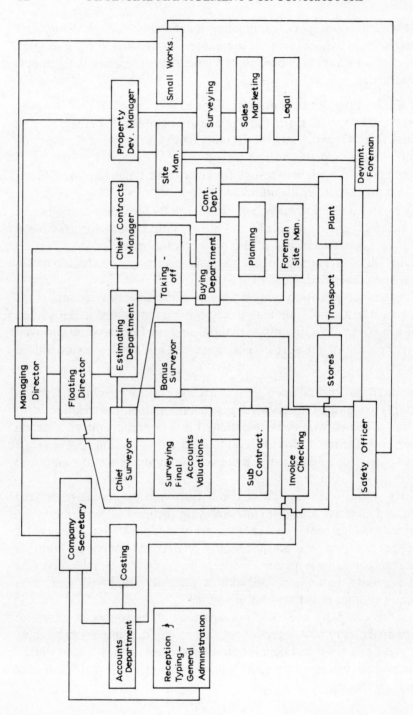

Fig. 1.1 Departmental structure

- Money. Salary, expenses, and use of a company car. In fact company cars can be a sore point with staff and must be allocated as equitably as possible; justice must be seen to be done and promises must be kept.
- Position. An individual's status and the related prestige enjoyed can be very important, as is evidenced by the translation of general foreman into site agent, site manager, or construction manager.
- Job security. This is an important consideration with many staff. Yearly interviews with senior management can be a useful time for inspiring confidence, and for many people pensions can also be an important consideration.
- Fear of change. As members of staff get older there is often a tendency to resent changes in company structure or introduction of new ideas. Equally, for some people even moving desks or changing offices can be a traumatic experience and management in those circumstances should take care to explain policy and give reassurances where necessary.
- Job satisfaction. Although perhaps the most significant factor, it will be difficult for management to achieve job satisfaction for all members of staff. For example, to translate the function of invoice checking into a rewarding and enjoyable task must be a management challenge. If achieved, the employee will be motivated and the company reduce costs.

Management must be aware of these factors and create within the company opportunities for promotion and extension to an individual's experience. It has been said that you can't please all the people all the time, but to achieve a successful business, with staff who are enthusiastic, motivated, self-confident and with the company's interest at heart, management should aim to do just this.

Some companies at this stage in their development expand horizontally into other fields such as hotels, time-sharing holiday accommodation and garages, or vertically into quarrying and mineral extraction, builders' merchants, plant, transport or waste management. The merits of such diversification are interesting, but outside the scope of this book.

NATIONAL CONTRACTORS/DEVELOPERS

The ultimate in the pattern of growth for construction companies is to attain national status and become a household name, such as Wimpey, Bovis, Costain, Laing or Barratt. Many companies expand their operations overseas into the international construction market, including civil and offshore engineering.

A company of this size is very differently structured to those so far discussed, with economies of scale and the opportunity to have research and development facilities and develop service departments or compan-

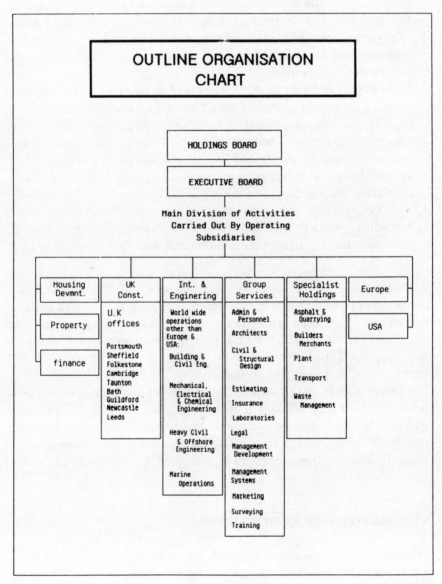

Fig. 1.2   Outline organisation chart

ies. Moreover, there will be extensive opportunities for horizontal or vertical expansion into other branches of industry.

The normal structure is a grouping of individual companies under a parent or holding company. The holding company may act as a banker for the group and also co-ordinate service companies such as finance, plant and transport. Inevitably, development will be separated from contracting, although the contracting division may build under contract for the development division (see Fig. 1.2). When groups operate across the UK it is common practice to have regional offices administered by a regional director. The structure of such regional offices may often be similar to that of medium-sized companies, but with the administrative back-up and financial expertise of a large company (see Fig. 1.3).

Most national companies will have solved the majority of the financial management problems outlined in this book and will have detailed

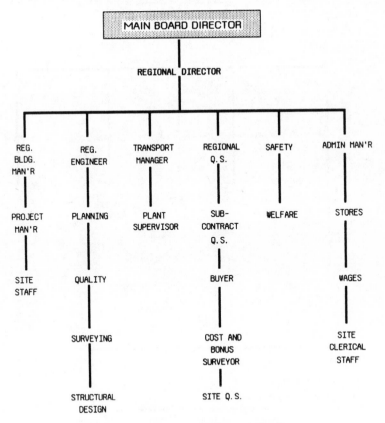

Fig. 1.3 Typical regional office organisation

administrative procedures for accurate cost value reconciliation, valuation of work in progress, cost targets, planning and programming, and for arranging finance and insurance. Printed formats will be used for management accounting which will ensure that detailed and accurate assessments are made of input figures. Obviously such sophisticated procedures absorb staff resources and only national companies can afford the luxury of the overhead costs involved. The only possible danger of such sophisticated management accounts is that junior staff do not understand the financial significance of their input and may make accidental, careless or deliberate errors. Equally, site management may sometimes for a variety of reasons have a vested interest in amending input, for example to under- or over-declare profit.

Within national companies the function of management can become

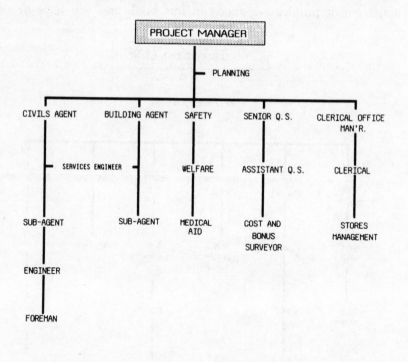

Fig. 1.4 Typical site organisation

very specialised and staff may have less opportunity to develop the wide experience that may be acquired in smaller organisations. Buying, for example, could be subdivided into taking-off and scheduling, obtaining quotations and placing orders, checking invoices and co-ordinating group purchasing. For this reason qualified trainees joining national contractors are usually given time in various departments before specialisation, with the object of gaining as wide an appreciation as possible of the structure of the group and job opportunities within it.

National development companies, although well known, may have fairly small organisational structures, particularly if the construction work is sub-contracted to other building companies. Many are nationally recognised, not necessarily because of their size but due to the level of their advertising.

Obviously, national contractors are most likely to concentrate on large, prestigious projects and in such cases the bulk of the routine administration and surveying will be undertaken via a site organisation. A typical structure is shown in Fig. 1.4. It should perhaps be noted that to a great extent contractors in a particular grouping tend to compete with each other rather than with those in the group above or below. In times of recession, however, national contractors via their regional offices will be prepared to tender for smaller contracts, thus increasing the pressure to reduce prices. Normally, however, the companies in the lower grouping have lower overheads and are therefore able to maintain a competitive edge.

2 Sources of Finance and Cash Flow

INTRODUCTION

A builder's capital can be simply identified either as owner's funds or as a debt. The owner's funds, or equity capital, are essentially risk capital and the investor has no guarantee that he will receive payment for the use of his money. Equally, the whole of the net profits of a company, after payment of creditors, tax and interest on debts, accrue to the equity holders, either in the form of a dividend on shareholding, or as retained profits in the business.

In this chapter an examination is made of both the equity capital and the main sources of finance available to the builder. In addition the movement of money through the business (the cash flow) is analysed because of its importance in giving early warning of impending cash shortages, or favourable balances, thus assisting in the projection of future borrowing needs.

EQUITY CAPITAL

A company's risk capital is divided into a defined number of shares. This share capital can be separated into several classes of share, the most common of which are preference shares, ordinary shares and deferred shares.

PREFERENCE SHARES

Preference shares entitle the shareholder to a priority in payment of dividend before it is paid on other types of share. The shareholder may also have priority in the repayment of capital in the event of the liquidation of the company. Holders of preference shares do not normally have a right to vote at general meetings of the company.

The shares may be cumulative or non-cumulative. Both entitle the shareholder to a fixed rate of dividend out of the profits each year. However, in the event of no dividend being declared in a year, those with cumulative preference shares have the additional right to have any arrears of dividend paid out of future profits before dividend is paid to other classes of share.

ORDINARY SHARES

Ordinary shares are held by shareholders who are entitled to the divisible profits remaining after any prior interests have been met. Normally ordinary shares carry full voting rights in proportion to the number of shares held. Some companies also issue deferred shares which entitle the holder to a dividend only after profits have reached a predetermined level or after a specified date, although sometimes larger dividends may be paid than to ordinary shareholders.

RETAINED PROFITS

A substantial proportion of the capital needed to fund a company can be accumulated in the form of reserves. Reserves are built up from residual profits not distributed in dividend to the shareholders, from a surplus resulting from revaluation of the assets of a company, or from any premiums received from the issue of shares at a price above the par value.

The combined amount of the issued share capital and the reserves are referred to as the 'shareholders' funds' or the 'capital base' of the company.

BONUS SHARES AND RIGHTS ISSUE

Many companies reach a situation where the retained profits or reserves, which have been ploughed back into the business, come close to equalling or exceeding the share capital. In such cases, companies may decide to make a bonus or capitalisation issue of shares to their shareholders, free of charge. In theory, as the capital base of the company has remained unchanged, the value of the increased number of shares held by the shareholder remains constant. In practice, however, the company will probably continue to pay the same dividend on the increased share capital, and thus the total shareholding will tend to increase in value.

Companies may seek to raise additional capital by offering new shares to their shareholders at a discount on the market price, particularly because the value of the original shares will tend to fall in value. The issue, known as a rights issue, is usually made on the basis of one new share for a given number of existing shares, such as one for three, one for four, or other variations. The shareholders, however, do not have to take up their rights to additional shares. A rights issue will generally be underwritten in a similar way to a new issue.

EXTERNAL SOURCES OF FINANCE

External sources of finance are normally due to be repaid according to an agreed programme, or after a defined period has elapsed. Lending may be secured by a fixed charge on certain specified assets, or a floating charge on the whole of the assets of a business, or it may be unsecured. Lenders will generally assume less risk than equity investors because they will have preference over equity holders in any claim resulting from failure of the business.

Lending is usually described as short, medium or long term depending upon the length of time before repayment is due. Typically, short term refers to sums borrowed for under 3 years including overdrafts, medium term to sums borrowed for periods of 3 to 10 years, and long term for periods exceeding 10 years. Money borrowed for less than 12 months, and trade credit, may be described as temporary debt.

COMMERCIAL BANKS

The bulk of the commercial banking business in England and Wales is undertaken by the members of the Committee of London Clearing Banks, namely Barclays, Lloyds, Midland and National Westminster, commonly known as the 'big four', who between them have over 12000 branches. Other banks and institutions, including The Royal Bank of Scotland, and Co-operative Bank and the Trustee Savings Bank, also have access to clearing facilities.

The two principal services the banks provide are, first, a place of security where companies or individuals can lodge their money balances, drawing on these as required and second, the provision of credit by extending loans to their customers.

The commercial banks up to the early 1970s concentrated their lending on short-term finance, usually in the form of overdraft facilities for working capital. In recent years, they have become more flexible and over 40% of non-personal lending is now medium or long term.

For business finance the banks offer the simplest and most convenient source of funds at competitive rates of interest. In view of this fact they have become the prime source of loan capital for the majority of companies. The operation of a bank account is considered in detail later in this chapter.

MERCHANT BANKS

Historically many of the merchant banks originated in the 19th century from merchant houses which traded throughout the world. In the course of time, by accepting bills of exchange to finance the trade of other merchants, they became involved in banking activities as 'accepting houses'.

Merchant banks also contribute to company finance by providing capital through sponsoring and underwriting the issue of stocks and shares. This has resulted in their being commonly known as 'accepting or issuing houses'. Sixteen of the leading merchant banks are members of the representative body, 'the accepting houses committee', and include such well-known banks as Baring Brothers, Hambros, Hill Samuel and Rothschild. Merchant banks carry out ordinary banking business, accepting deposits from other banks or companies in the UK or overseas, and lending money usually in the medium-term market to British companies.

In the construction industry merchant banks will provide finance for residential, office and industrial development. Usually money is only lent against specific projects and a formal mortgage deed is taken out by the bank as a first charge on the land or property. The borrower will be required to pay all the legal fees incurred by the bank and a surveyor's valuation fee. Often the bank will charge a commitment fee of approximately 1% of the maximum advance that is offered and possibly an additional negotiation fee of up to a further 1%.

Interest charges are usually higher than those levied by the commercial banks and range from $4\frac{1}{2}\%$ to $5\frac{1}{2}\%$ over base rate (i.e. the base rate of a named commercial bank). The interest will be paid quarterly in arrears at the prevailing rate, and be subject to a minimum but no maximum rate.

Merchant banks are usually prepared to advance a larger proportion of the total cost of a project than the commercial banks and a typical structure for a residential scheme would be:

(a) Initial advance of two-thirds of the land value which may be more or less than the cost to the company of the site.

(b) Monthly payments of 75% of the building cost supported by a surveyor's valuation of the work in progress.

(c) Repayments of 85% of sale proceeds as each house is sold.

The repayment structure geared to house sales will normally result in the maximum possible borrowing reaching only 60% or 70% of the advance agreed. This in effect increases the percentage cost of the commitment and other fees.

In certain circumstances where the bank considers that it is being asked to bear an abnormal risk, it may require a share in the return of, say, 25% of the net profit, but it will not accept any responsibility for a loss.

The bank will require the borrower to submit a feasibility study and profit forecast for the project, together with full details of the company's financial affairs, including:

- the audited company accounts for at least the last three years' trading and interim financial accounts where available
- internal management accounts, and cash flow forecasts for the project and the company
- a schedule of other borrowing by the company

Any offer of finance will be for a definite period of years, but it may be possible to extend the loan to cover any outstanding balance due to lack of sales.

In addition to the activities outlined, merchant banks are also involved in leasing, hire purchase, insurance broking, shipping and property management and act as advisers on a wide range of company problems, including capital reorganisation, dividend policy, mergers and acquisitions.

FINANCE HOUSES

Finance houses provide the credit required for hire purchase of plant, machinery, scaffolding, office equipment and cars. Such facilities may be offered direct by a finance house to a contractor or via the company supplying the goods or equipment. Under the terms of all hire purchase agreements the ownership of the goods rests with the finance house until all the payments by instalment have been made, and the buyer then exercises his option to purchase. Goods, therefore, cannot be used as security for loans from other business houses until the hire purchase agreement has been discharged. A finance house normally requires a percentage deposit and repayment by monthly instalments over a stipulated period of years.

The government have periodically regulated both the amount of the deposit and the repayment period in order to control the growth of credit nationally. Interest charges vary and extremely competitive rates may be negotiated if a company places all their hire-purchase business with one, or at the most two, finance houses. Even where the supplier acts as an agent for the finance house, the interest rate charged can be the subject of negotiation within defined limits. Charges are stated as a percentage over the finance house base rate, and can be as low as 1%.

Hire purchase is widely used by contractors to provide finance and has the added advantage of low deposits and competitive interest charges. Less important are credit sale agreements, where the buyer and seller enter into a contract for the sale of goods by instalment when ownership of the goods rests with the buyer.

INVESTMENT TRUSTS, INSURANCE COMPANIES, PENSION FUNDS, BUILD-ING SOCIETIES

These financial institutions have been grouped together as they are all significant suppliers of long-term capital and channel the savings of the man-in-the-street into secure investments with potential for capital growth. Funds are invested not only in stocks, shares and government securities, but also directly into the property market where long-term money tends to be matched with long-term liabilities.

Interest charges reflect trends of the past and the predictions for the future and in consequence they can vary substantially from the prevailing bank rates. These institutions may provide development finance at higher rates of interest in line with those of merchant banks, with an option on completion either to convert the loan into long-term borrowing or to purchase the development for the institution's investment portfolio. In either case there will usually be a requirement for the property to be let to a financially sound tenant, before the option can be exercised.

PRIVATE AND DIRECTORS' LOANS

Loans may be available from the directors of a company, relations or acquaintances. Such funds tend to be commonly used within smaller companies, although the loan will often be unsecured and arranged on an informal basis. Care should therefore be taken to agree and record in writing the method and date for repayment, and the basis of calculating interest charges.

TRADE CREDIT

The majority of builders' merchants operate a monthly account system where goods delivered to the builder in one calendar month are not required to be paid for until the end of the following month. Such credit facilities are a considerable financial help to the builder and provide, on average, 46 days' free credit. In addition many merchants provide a cash or settlement discount of $2\frac{1}{2}\%$ provided the contractor pays the account by the agreed date, or an even higher discount for earlier settlement. Where such discounts are not available, or offered, many companies will delay payment for an additional two, three, or more weeks, thus extending their credit facilities to well over two months. The national companies with bulk purchasing powers will attempt to negotiate with merchants for longer periods of credit without loss of discount. With the high levels of interest prevailing, such negotiations have been resisted and agreements made in earlier years have often been rescinded. Companies short of cash will arrange deliveries early rather than late in the month, in order to extend their credit. Consequently if credit facilities were withdrawn, or restricted, many firms would find themselves in extreme financial difficulties, because of this reliance on trade credit.

INVOICE DISCOUNTING

Book debts can be converted into cash by borrowing up to 75% of the value of invoices raised by the company from a finance house. The cost of discounting invoices can be high and has the added disadvantage that the company is still responsible for collection of the debt.

FACTORING

This is a similar process to invoice discounting, except that the factoring company or finance house assumes complete responsibility for the credit risk. The factoring company provides cash to the full value of the invoice, less only a servicing discount, as soon as the invoice is prepared. They also provide the ancillary services of credit control, sales accounting and debt collection. Such companies, with no direct contact with the client, will not hesitate to employ debt collection agencies, particularly as any bad debts that arise are chargeable against the factoring company. Invoice discounting and factoring are more widely used by manufacturers than construction companies, but where they are used they provide cash at least four weeks earlier than could otherwise be expected.

LEASING

Plant, machinery and cars can be leased as an alternative to hire purchase. Such leasing agreements may also include provision for regular maintenance, repair and replacement with new equipment at regular intervals. Comparison of the total cost with other methods of finance will need careful appraisal and specialist advice should be obtained due to the frequent changes in financial legislation and tax concessions. Offices and premises may also be leased or rented to avoid tying up a company's capital. The disadvantage is that buildings tend to appreciate in value and they could have been used as security for a bank overdraft or other loan.

LEASE BACK

An arrangement can be made where the premises or property used by a builder is sold to a financial institution with the agreement that the company can lease back the property, either indefinitely or for a fixed period of time, under a normal lease agreement. Such an arrangement could release substantial amounts of cash for reinvestment. In certain circumstances it would also be possible to arrange to buy back the property at the future market value or an agreed sum, at a later date. Lease back agreements may also be applied to plant, machinery and transport owned by a company, subject to valuation.

REALISATION OF ASSETS

Cash may be raised at short notice by liquidation or sale of assets, such as land, property, plant, transport and stocks of materials, owned by the company. Once such assets have been sold, they can no longer be used to support borrowing from the commercial banks. One danger of raising cash in this way on a large scale is that the company's creditors may interpret the action as an indication of liquidity problems and press for early settlement of outstanding debts, or restrict credit. Rumours concerning a company's liquidity rapidly circulate and often result in precipitate action by creditors, who are anxious to protect their interests in the uncertain economic conditions which sometimes prevail.

STAGE PAYMENTS

It is common practice in the construction industry for the contractor to receive payments from the client as the work proceeds. Payments may be related to the stage of work completed, for example, sub-structure, external walls, roof and plastering, or alternatively payments may be required at regular intervals, on the basis of the value of the work completed. Contractors often use methods such as front-end loading, to improve their cash flow and ensure that the valuation of work in progress is substantially in excess of the respective cost. Front-end loading is discussed in more detail later in this chapter, and in Chapter 10.

THE OPERATION OF A BANK ACCOUNT

Before approaching the bank, the prospective borrower will need to analyse the following questions:

- Why is the finance required?
- How much finance is required?
- How and when is the money to be repaid?
- Will the company be able to cope with financial reverses during the period of the loan, without recourse to further borrowing?
- What security can be offered to the bank?

Having considered these questions the borrower will be in a position to discuss the financial requirements with the bank.

INFORMATION REQUIRED

Normally negotiations with the bank will take place on at least an annual basis. Prior to the bank considering an offer of finance, certain basic information will be required:

- a copy of the audited financial accounts, for the company's last three years of trading
- interim financial accounts and current management accounts
- a forecast of anticipated profit on contracts and/or development
- cash flow forecast
- a schedule of stocks of land and property, showing cost and current value, excluding any charged to other financial institutions
- a schedule of work in progress on development sites, less any cash received on account
- a schedule of fixed assets and equipment

- a schedule of borrowings from other financial institutions
- capital expenditure plans

In addition, the bank will examine and appraise the calibre and integrity of the directors of the company, the management structure and its resilience to change, the aims and objectives of the company and its approach to stock and credit control, over-trading and external economic pressures.

It is also important to appreciate that the bank keeps detailed records of each visit by the directors of a company to its offices and that, all too quickly, next year's projections will become last year's results. Trust and personal relationships are therefore extremely important in any negotiations.

SECURITY

The bank will examine the information provided and identify adequate security to set against the borrowing requirements.

Preferred security will take the form of land, property and work in progress. The bank will usually lend up to 50% of the value of such assets. At first glance this would seem to represent a wide margin of safety, but the dramatic fall in values after the financial crisis of 1973 demonstrated that this was not an over-generous assessment. Moreover, the bank is not providing risk capital and has a duty to safeguard the deposits of other customers. The bank, consequently, does not normally expect to fund a company to a greater extent than the owners of the business, but nevertheless, might do so in certain circumstances. The total bank borrowing, therefore, will normally not exceed the capital originally invested, plus retained profits and reserves.

It will usually be a condition of borrowing that the bank take out a floating charge, or debenture, on all the assets of a company, and individual mortgages on all land and property. In addition, if the company is part of a group of companies, the bank will require cross-guarantees. This means that each company in a group guarantees to the bank that it will meet the liabilities incurred by any other company in the group.

In the case of private companies, with insufficient assets to support their borrowing requirement, it is fairly common for the bank to require one or more directors to personally guarantee the bank borrowing. Great care should be exercised in entering into such agreements, particularly where directors are minority shareholders.

Borrowing facilities

The bank normally offers a wide range of alternative funding arrangements, of which the most common are overdraft facilities, medium- or long-term finance, and contract guarantee or performance bonds. The main banks also have corporate finance departments or subsidiaries who function as merchant banks. The local bank manager will therefore often assist a company in obtaining equity or long-term capital.

Overdraft facilities

A bank overdraft is the most widely used form of short-term finance for funding day-to-day financial commitments of a business, on the understanding that:

(a) The overdraft will not be used for capital commitments without the bank's prior consent.

(b) Interest will be calculated on the amount outstanding on a daily basis and charged to the account quarterly. Arrangement fees, service charges and commitment fees on undrawn facilities may be charged, but are generally small.

(c) The interest rate charged is subject to negotiation and will usually be approximately 3% above the base rate. However, the rate actually charged depends on the nature and status of the borrower and may range from 1% above the base rate for companies of the highest standing, to 5% above the base rate for small private companies. (NB: The base rate is a bank's base lending rate to which most of its lending is linked, and is published nationally.)

(d) The total amount of the outstanding overdraft is repayable at any time on demand, which is of course a disadvantage to the borrower.

(e) The facility will be subject to periodical reviews at least annually and, provided the borrower is credit-worthy, will generally be continued from year to year.

Medium- and long-term finance

Medium-term loans will be made available for specific expenditure on capital commitments, such as land, property, plant and machinery. The bank will have different types of loan accounts to meet a variety of needs. The repayments may be monthly, quarterly, yearly or at the end of an agreed period. Interest will be charged at a percentage either above the bank's base lending rate or more commonly above the London Interbank

Offered Rate (LIBOR). The LIBOR rate more accurately reflects the cost of funds to the bank, especially for medium-term loans. It is the rate of interest at which funds are offered on loan for a specified period in the London Interbank market.

The interest rate tends to be from $\frac{1}{2}\%$ to 1% more than that charged for an overdraft facility, and this is from $1\frac{1}{2}\%$ to 6% above LIBOR rate. Moreover, as the LIBOR rate varies from minute to minute throughout the day, it is necessary for a time and date to be agreed at which interest will be charged.

Performance bonds
Many clients, including local authorities, require contract guarantee or performance bonds. Such bonds are usually required to cover 10% of the contract sum and the bank or specialist bond company guarantee the client against loss, up to the amount of the bond, in the event of the builder failing to meet his contractual obligations.

The bank may agree a bond limit subject to the value of any bonds arranged being deducted from the overdraft facility. The rate charged is usually 1% per annum of the bond limit.

MONITORING OF THE ACCOUNT
Once a loan or overdraft facility has been made available to a company, the bank maintains a close watch on the operation of the account and monitors the movement of cash through the account. In particular:

(a) The total debited is deducted from the total credited each month and the balance is compared with the cash flow forecast for that month.
(b) The opening balance is compared to the closing balance each month, which will indicate the long-term trend.
(c) The headroom or gap between the maximum borrowing in a month and the limit of the overdraft facility is monitored for long-term trends. The bank will be concerned to see that both full use is made of the funds allocated and that enough headroom exists on the account to meet monthly financial pressures.
(d) The swing or difference between minimum and maximum borrowing in the month is compared to earlier months. The swing will tend to disappear from the account where hard core borrowing (minimum borrowing) is increasing each month and the company, in order to maintain headroom within the overdraft facility, delays payments until cash is received.

CASH FLOW FORECASTING

A cash flow forecast is a statement of the estimated cash receipts and payments projected over a future period. The forecast can give early indication of shortages or surplus of cash and therefore gives time to:

- Assess and arrange borrowing requirements
- Adjust programmes of work to equalise borrowing and avoid peak demand
- implement credit control and monitor outstanding monies due
- reduce or increase expenditure
- move surplus funds to an interest-bearing account. In the case of large sums of money this may be on an 'overnight' basis

The cash flow forecast does not give any indication of profit or loss, although both profit and loss affect cash balances.

Cash flow forecasting has only become widely used in the UK during the last 15 years, primarily under the impetus of the banks who have insisted that companies provide such forecasts as part of the information required when negotiating for overdraft facilities or loans. The banks were aware that it would be difficult if not impossible in the construction industry to achieve any degree of accuracy, but the banks' primary objective was to encourage their customers to think of future commitments and their impact on cash balances.

The banks have prepared standard forms to assist their clients in the preparation of cash flow forecasts (see Fig. 2.1 for a typical example). Such forms need to be adapted for use by developers or builders.

DEFINITION OF CASH

The term 'cash' is not strictly accurate in that the cash flow forecast is concerned with the date on which transactions are debited or credited to the bank account. The date on which sales are invoiced or expenses incurred and cash or cheques received or paid out is, therefore, not relevant.

Book entries such as internal plant hire, stores, depreciation, etc, should not be included in the forecast.

CASH BOOK

The cash book of a company indicates the apparent balance at the bank, but does not make any allowance for the time taken to clear cheques.

Cheques or cash paid into the company's own branch or sub-branch

Cashflow Forecast For name of company, firm etc

For the period From To

Branch

Enter month													Total	
	Projected	Actual	Projected	Actual	Projected	Actual	Projected	Actual	Projected	Actual	Projected	Actual	Projected	Actual
Receipts														
Sales – Cash														
Sales – Debtors														
Loans														
Other receipts														
A Total receipts														
Payments														
Cash purchases														
To creditors														
Wages and salaries (net)														
PAYE/NIC														
Capital items														
Rent/rates														
Services														
HP/leasing repayments														
Bank/finance charges														
Loan repayments														
VAT (net)														
Corporation tax, etc														
Dividend														
B Total payments														
Opening bank balance														
Add to B if overdrawn Subtract from B if credit														
C Total														
D Closing bank balance (Difference between A&C)														

Fig. 2.1 Standard cash flow for each form

will be credited the same day. Cheques or cash received and paid into a different branch of the bank, even in the same locality, will take 3 to 7 days to clear. Payments made by cheque will also take 3 to 7 days to clear. Moreover, when posted, either first or second class, the amount of the cheque will not be debited to the bank account for from 4 to 14 days. In normal circumstances, therefore, the cash book of a company will show a more pessimistic view of the cash balance at the bank than is actually the case.

It is highly likely that the joint stock banks will computerise the clearing procedures, which will result in all cheques, debits and credits being cleared in one day.

POSITIVE CASH FLOW, INCOME, RECEIPTS
Income in the construction industry can come from a wide variety of sources, with varying periods of delay. It will be helpful, therefore, to identify the most significant of these.

Valuations of work in progress
Where work is carried out, for example, under the terms of the Standard Form of Building Contract JCT 80, interim payments are made by the client to the contractor. These payments are for the value of work completed, less previous payments under the contract and less a maximum retention of 5%.

In effect, the work executed in the previous month is valued at the end of the period by the quantity surveyor, in order to ascertain the amount to be included in the interim certificate issued by the architect.

The preparation of the valuation and issue of the interim certificate may take up to 7 days. The contractor is entitled to payment within 14 days from the date of issue, making a total delay of 21 days. In practice, payment will vary from at best 3 to 4 days, to at worst 28 days after the date of the valuation.

Progress payments are extremely important to the contractor's cash flow. In fact it is probable that, provided a reasonable level of profit is maintained throughout the contract period, after the first two or three months, a positive cash flow can be maintained.

Stage payments
The contractor may request payments at various stages of completion of the work, such as foundations, external walls, roof or plastering. Such

arrangements would normally apply to smaller contracts and possibly to design and build projects and residential development.

The delay in payment will depend on the client's representatives, the financial integrity of the client and any arrangements made at the inception of the contract.

Release of retention

The retention that is held during the progress of the contract is released in two stages. Fifty per cent is released at practical completion of the work and the balance when all defects arising during the defects liability period have been made good. It may be necessary for the credit control department of the contractor to ensure prompt release of retentions.

Final accounts

The final account is due for completion usually within six months from practical completion. In practice settlement of the final account is often substantially delayed. The contractor through his surveying department should take all steps to mitigate delays by providing the client's quantity surveyor with all necessary information promptly, and regularly press for completion of the account.

House sales

Where a building company undertakes housing development, cash flow will originate from the proceeds of sale at the legal completion of each dwelling. The builder's solicitor customarily deducts his own fee and often also the estate agent's commission from the sale proceeds, before forwarding the balance by post or by hand to the builder.

Developers are sometimes able to negotiate that the 10% deposit paid by the purchaser on exchange of contracts is paid to them direct, instead of the more usual practice of the solicitor holding it as stakeholder in his 'client account'.

In preparing cash flow forecasts it is extremely difficult to predict the date of house sales with any degree of accuracy. Where, however, a company concentrates its output on the first-time buyer market and arranges mortgages on behalf of the purchaser, it may be possible to achieve reasonably accurate forecasts.

Rents
Rents from investment property are normally received on quarter days.

Loans from other financial institutions
Where loans have been arranged, for example, on residential or commercial development, the monthly or other periodic payments are treated as income on the cash flow forecast.

VAT refund
The majority of construction work, except for repair work and maintenance, is currently zero rated for VAT purposes, but contractors are required to pay VAT (currently 15%) on the cost of materials and plant hire. The VAT paid each month has to be reclaimed from the VAT office at Southend. A company with an annual new build turnover of £10 000 000 will be claiming VAT refund of approximately £50 000 per month. Normally payment is delayed for two weeks after submission of the claim. Additional delays may occur in the post or through industrial action.

Sale of stock, plant, land, property or other assets
Income from this source may arise during the normal course of business, but if such sales are forced by circumstances, rumours of financial instability may develop and affect other aspects of the business, such as trade credit.

Front-end loading
The contractor, when pricing the bill of quantities, adjusts the rates in order to transfer profit or even cost of operations undertaken towards the end of the contract to earlier operations, for example substructure or concrete work. Profit and costs, alternatively, are concentrated on certain items in the preliminaries such as scaffolding, on the assumption that the client's quantity surveyor will value on a priced basis. The rates shown against items in the priced bill of quantities become contract rates once the contract is made. Front-end loading is also outlined in Chapter 10.

The effect of such adjustments is that during the early valuations of a contract an enhanced cash flow is achieved and the contractor will have the advantage of forward funding throughout virtually the whole contract period. For example, a contract of £1 200 000 in value is to be executed in 12 months. The gross profit of 10%, £120 000, is front-loaded into the first three valuations. The company will have the use of a substantial portion of this money throughout the contract period.

Some national contractors have substantial positive cash flows of many millions of pounds from their contracting operations as a result of the combination of front-end loading and favourable credit arrangements (see Chapters 4 and 10).

NEGATIVE CASH FLOW, EXPENDITURE, PAYMENTS

The majority of items of overhead expenditure can be clearly identified with regard to both the time of payment and value, i.e. salaries, rent, rates, insurance, postage and telephone, capital purchases, hire purchase instalments and loan repayments.

When preparing cash flow forecasts for trading expenditure, the value can be assessed by reference to the contract programme and computer predictions from typical previous contract performance. The analysis of trading expenditure, shown in Fig. 2.2, demonstrates that the weighted average delay in payments is 33.5 days or 4.8 weeks.

TIME INTERVALS

Cash flows can be prepared for a daily, weekly or monthly time interval, but the most common period used by builders is monthly. The total receipts expected in the month are compared with the anticipated expenditure. The forecast, therefore, will indicate the average monthly overdraft or balance, but will not highlight the swing on the account:

	£
Opening overdraft	10 000
Receipts	8 000
Expenditure	7 000
Closing overdraft	9 000

Therefore, the swing on the bank account during the month could be from a maximum overdraft of £17 000 to a minimum of £9 000, or alternatively from a minimum of £2 000 to a maximum of £9 000.

A weekly cash flow forecast would highlight these cash movements but most companies would be unable to devote the necessary resources to achieving this degree of accuracy for a year ahead. Any detailed study of cash flow patterns on contracts would need to be analysed on a weekly basis and the results applied to the regular monthly forecast.

Cost section	Terms of payment	Average delay (days)	Cheque clearance	Cumulative average delay	Estimated proportion of total cost (%)	Weighted average delay (days)
Direct labour	weekly	1-14 average 7	cash	7 days	6	0.42
Labour only subcontractors	weekly	1-14 average 7	3 days	10 days	15	1.5
Labour and material subcontractors	weekly/ monthly	1-30 average 15	incl postage say 5 days	20 days	22	4.4
Nominated subcontractors	J.C.T 17 days after date of cert	(1-30)+24 average 39	5 days	44 days	20	8.8
Materials (with discount)	monthly account	(1-30)+30 average 45	5 days	50 days	18	9.0
Materials (without discount)	monthly account	(1-30)+40 average 55	5 days	60 days	8	4.8
Nominated suppliers	J.C.T.	(1-30)+30 average 45	5 days	50 days	5	2.5
Plant hire	monthly/ monthly account	(1-30)+15 average 30	5 days	35 days	6	2.1
Own stores and internal plant hire	Not included as purchased separately			TOTAL	100	33.52

Fig. 2.2 Analysis of trading expenditure

SHORT-TERM CASH FLOW FORECAST

In view of the fact that the monthly cash flow forecast only provides a limited indication of the swing on the bank account, the company can monitor the cash book on a daily basis. A short-term cash flow can then be provided each week or month for the succeeding four weeks, outlining the daily movements of 'cash' expected.

It is usually possible to predict cash flow, with reasonable accuracy, for short periods of time and this will, of course, be particularly useful if headroom on the bank account is restricted. Short-term cash flows should, of course, be compared with the long-term company cash flow and adjustments made where necessary.

DURATION OF CASH FLOW

Cash flows can be prepared for any period of time. Individual contract or development cash flows will usually be prepared for the duration of the project. The company or *master* cash flow will usually be prepared for one year ahead. Accuracy will obviously diminish with time as the number of uncertainties increases and the calculations become more nebulous; for example, contract or development start dates, rate of sale on residential development sites, changes in interest rates and other overhead commitments and inflation.

MONITORING CASH FLOW

The monitoring of actual cash flow for a particular project within a medium-sized contractor is fraught with difficulty. Problems arise because it is normal accounting practice to maintain financial accounts with a bought ledger with separate records for each merchant. Payment to the merchant will not, however, be identified between contracts. In fact, to monitor cash flow for each project would need a separate set of *cash accounts*. Cash flow, therefore, is monitored by reference to the cost accounts. Accurate information may be limited to the cost breakdown available.

It should be noted that if materials are costed separately for each contract it will be difficult to identify the actual date payments pass through the bank account for discount and non-discount cheques.

Thus where cost accounts are used, reference can be made to the average delay expected, and an appropriate assessment made. With larger companies, there would be some advantage in maintaining separate bank accounts and as a consequence separate ledger accounts for different

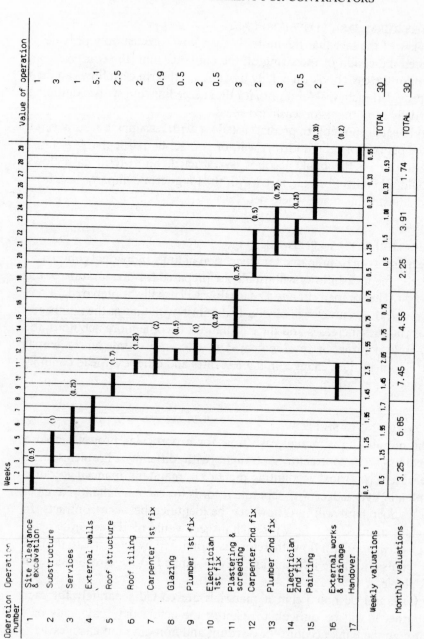

Fig. 2.3 Contract programme (value in thousands)

activities of the business, e.g. contracting, small works, housing development, and industrial development. The overall cash flow and capital use
by each section of the company can then be clearly identified. Cost
accounts are examined in detail in Chapter 9.

The company cash flow as revealed by the bank statement can usefully
be recorded in graph form in order that long-term trends can be identified
clearly and quickly.

PREPARATION OF CASH FLOW FORECAST

In order to prepare a cash flow forecast for a company, it is first necessary
to prepare individual cash flows for each contract or development. The
individual forecasts will be summarised to provide departmental cash
flows which in turn will be amalgamated into the *company* or *master* cash
flow. The master cash flow will also provide for general overheads which
cannot be allocated to individual projects. In very large companies a
separate overhead cash flow may be necessary.

Contract programme

The first stage in the preparation of the cash flow is to obtain or prepare
the contract programme, preferably in the form of a bar chart. A simple
illustration of the construction of a house has been used as an example,
and the contract programme is shown in Fig. 2.3.

The value of each operation has to be identified from the bill of
quantities or, if this is not available, from the contractor's estimate. The
estimated weekly and monthly valuation of the construction work can
then be calculated.

Analysis of value and cost

The second stage in the preparation of the forecast is to analyse the value
and cost of the project. In this exercise the following assumptions have
been made:

(a) Valuations have been prepared accurately and the estimate or bill of
quantities has not been front-end loaded.
(b) Gross profit margin before adjustment of overheads is 10%.
(c) Overheads are included separately on master cash flow.
(d) Retention of 5% is applied under JCT 80 conditions.
(e) Valuations are monthly on the last day of the calendar month and are
paid by client within 21 days of date of valuation.

Week no	Gross valuation	Net valuation cash inflow	Cost of labour	Cash outflow	Cost of plant and materials	Cash outflow	Balance at bank
1			0.18				--
2			0.18	0.18			(0.18)
3			0.36	0.18			(0.36)
4	3.25		0.45	0.36	1.75		(0.72)
5			0.45	0.45			(1.17)
6			0.70	0.45			(1.62)
7		3.09	0.70	0.70			0.77
8	6.85		0.61	0.70	3.70		0.07
9			0.52	0.61		1.75	(2.29)
10			0.52	0.52			(2.81)
11		6.51	0.90	0.52			3.18
12	7.45		0.74	0.90	4.02		2.28
13			0.56	0.74		3.70	(2.16)
14			0.27	0.56			(2.72)
15		7.08	0.27	0.27			4.09
16			0.27	0.27			3.82
17	4.55		0.27	0.27	2.46		3.55
18			--	0.27		4.02	(0.74)
19			0.18	--			(0.74)
20		4.32	0.18	0.18			3.40
21	2.25		0.45	0.18	1.22		3.22
22			0.54	0.45		2.46	0.31
23			0.36	0.54			(0.23)
24		2.14	0.39	0.36			1.55
25	3.91		0.12	0.39	2.11		1.16
26			0.12	0.12		1.22	(0.18)
27			0.12	0.12			(0.30)
28		3.71	0.19	0.12			3.29
29			0.20	0.19			3.10
30	1.74			0.20	0.94		2.90
31						2.11	0.79
32							0.79
33		2.40					3.19
34							3.19
35						0.94	2.25
36							--
56		0.75					3.00
Totals	30	30	10.80	10.80	16.20	16.20	3.00

includes 50% retention (rows 31–34)

balance of retention (rows 35–56)

Labour 10.80 (40%) materials & plant 16.20 (60%) Profit 3.00 (10%)

Fig. 2.4   Analysis of value and cost (thousands)

(f) Cost has been confined to labour, materials and plant (40% labour and 60% materials and plant) to minimise calculations.

(g) Materials are delivered as required and not in advance.

(h) Materials and plant are on monthly account (see Fig. 2.2) and therefore payments will pass through the bank account five weeks or more after the date of the valuation.

The analysis has been prepared on a weekly basis to demonstrate the difference between weekly and monthly cash flows. The analysis of value and cost and resultant cash flow is shown in Fig. 2.4.

Cash flow graph

A graph of the estimated bank balance over the contract period is shown in Fig. 2.5. This graph demonstrates that within a few weeks of the commencement of the project a positive bank balance may occur for one or two weeks each month. Moreover, the actual capital needed to fund the project is not required continuously throughout the contract period and is a relatively small proportion of the contract sum. If the profit margin drops below 10% this will of course have a direct impact on the figures.

Cash flow forecast contract

A monthly cash flow forecast using the same basic information is shown in Fig. 2.6 and the corresponding graph of the average monthly bank balance over the contract period is shown in Fig. 2.7.

The point made earlier concerning the swing on the bank account can now be clearly seen. If, for example, the overdraft limit for the project is £1 000, the monthly forecast shows a borrowing requirement of £720. The weekly forecast, however, shows that the swing on the account will result in a borrowing requirement of £720 in month one, £1 600 in month two and £3 100 in month three, although in each case this will only be for a maximum of two weeks each month.

Cash flow forecast: Development

A second cash flow forecast (see Fig. 2.8) has been prepared using the same basic information, but with the following amendments:

(a) It is assumed that the opening bank overdraft is £11 500 and includes land, architects' and legal fees.

(b) Sale price for completed house is £50 000.

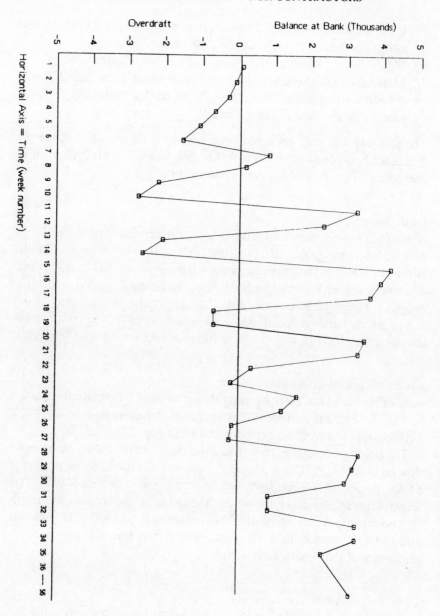

Fig. 2.5 Graph of estimated weekly bank balance

Month	1	2	3	4	5	6	7	8	9	→ 13
Expenditure										
Labour	0.72	2.30	2.55	2.11	0.63	1.74	0.75	--	--	
Materials and plant	--	--	1.75	3.70	4.02	2.46	1.22	2.11	0.94	0.75
Total	0.72	2.30	4.30	5.81	4.65	4.20	1.97	2.11	0.94	0.75
Income										
Valuation	--	3.09	6.51	7.08	4.32	2.14	3.71	1.65	--	
Release of retention								0.75	--	0.75
Total	--	3.09	6.51	7.08	4.32	2.14	3.71	2.40	--	0.75
Positive cash flow		0.79	2.21	1.27			1.74	0.29		
Negative cash flow	0.72				0.33	2.06			0.94	
Opening bank balance	--	(0.72)	0.07	2.28	3.55	3.22	1.16	2.90	3.19	2.25
Closing bank balance	(0.72)	0.07	2.28	3.55	3.22	1.16	2.90	3.19	2.25	3.00

N.B. The monthly cash flow forecast indicates the average overdraft or balance and does not necessarily highlight the swing in the account. No adjustment has been made for interest.

Fig. 2.6 Monthly cash flow forecast (contract) in thousands

(c) Legal completion takes place immediately following practical completion on site.

(d) Legal and estate agent's fees are £2000.

(e) Project is financed by the bank.

The dramatic difference between contract and *company-funded* development cash flows is clearly demonstrated. Obviously any delay in the sale of the house will have a continuing adverse effect on the borrowing requirement.

METHODS OF SIMPLIFICATION OF CONTRACT CASH FLOW

Contractors will need to prepare cash flows for each project at, at the least, three-monthly intervals. As an alternative to the detailed calculations outlined above, certain assumptions and simplifications can be introduced to reduce the time and effort taken to prepare cash flows.

Instead of the detailed evaluation of the contract programme, a microcomputer can be used to project the estimated monthly valuations over the contract period. The computer can be programmed to utilise actual valuations on previous contracts undertaken by the company and adjustments introduced for a variety of building forms and methods of construction. When produced in the form of a graph, value against time, such projections usually take the form of an 'S' curve. Calculations of cost or expenditure can be based on this same estimated valuation produced by the computer.

In the last two columns of Fig. 2.9 analysis of trading expenditure shows that a weighted average delay has been calculated at 33.5 days. The equivalent average delay in the monthly valuation is 36 days. Therefore, both average income and expenditure will apparently fall within the same calendar month for forecast purposes.

The use of such methods will of course distort the actual cash flow, as shown by the dotted line in Fig. 2.7. The distortion, however, is marginal. Using the above information as a base, an *event* cash flow could be prepared. The monthly income and expenditure can be assumed to balance except for certain adjustments or *events* such as:

(a) The retention which should be deducted from each valuation and the release of retention included at practical completion and at the end of making good defects.

(b) The estimated profit margin on the project.

(c) Estimating errors or incorrect pricing.

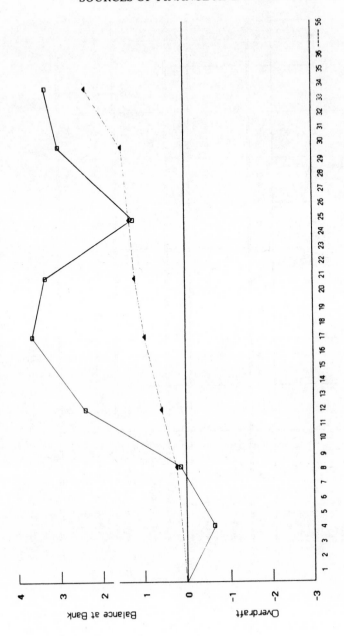

Horizontal Axis = Time (week number)

Fig. 2.7 Graph of average monthly bank balance (thousands)

Month	1	2	3	4	5	6	7	8	9
Expenditure									
Labour	0.72	2.30	2.55	2.11	0.63	1.74	0.75	--	--
Materials and plant	--	--	1.75	3.70	4.02	2.46	1.22	2.11	0.94
Fees							2.00		
Total	0.72	2.30	4.30	5.81	4.65	4.20	3.97	2.11	0.94
Income									
House sale							50.00		
Total							50.00		
Positive cash flow							46.03		
Negative cash flow	0.72	2.30	4.30	5.81	4.65	4.20		2.11	0.94
Opening bank balance	(11.50)	(12.22)	(14.52)	(18.82)	(24.63)	(29.28)	(33.48)	12.55	10.44
Closing bank balance	(12.22)	(14.52)	(18.82)	(24.63)	(29.28)	(33.48)	12.55	10.44	9.50

N.B. No adjustment has been made for interest or bank charges

Fig. 2.8   Monthly cash flow forecast (development) in thousands

Month	1	2	3	4	5	6	7	8	9	13
Expenditure	--	2.92	6.16	6.70	4.10	2.03	3.52	1.57		0.75
Income	--	3.09	6.51	7.08	4.32	2.14	3.71	2.40	--	
Positive cash flow	--	0.17	0.35	0.38	0.22	0.11				
Negative cash flow	--									
Opening bank balance	--	--	0.17	0.52	0.90	1.12	0.19	0.83	2.25	2.25
Closing bank balance	--	0.17	0.52	0.90	1.12	1.23	1.42	2.25	2.25	3.00

Fig. 2.9 Monthly cash flow forecast (contract) using weighted average delay

(d) Front-end loading or adjustment to preliminaries.
(e) Claims, remeasurement of provisional work, variation orders, etc. Delay in settlement of such items will reduce positive cash flow.
(f) VAT at 15% will be paid on all invoices for materials and plant hire and the corresponding credit received from the VAT office. In theory, these balancing positive and negative cash flows will occur within the same monthly period. If this is not the case an adjustment should be made.
(g) Over- or under-measurement of the work at the valuation (see Chapter 10 and 11).
(h) Adjustment for the expenditure in first month of contract excluded by use of the weighted average. Such adjustments could be made manually or by the use of a microcomputer.

CONCLUSION

Cash flow forecasting is an essential tool of the financial management of a company. Long-term cash flow forecasts provide essential guidance to management and indicate possible future shortfalls or surplus of cash. Regular updating of the cash flow forecast will ensure that sufficient time is available to meet such shortfalls and maintain liquidity. This will be accomplished by extending credit facilities, by arranging for additional borrowing, by delaying capital commitments or by amending work programmes.

Long-term cash flow forecasts do not indicate the likely movement of cash within a monthly period and, therefore, the total expenditure and total income in a month should be examined, to highlight the maximum and minimum overdraft that would *theoretically* be possible.

The use of the short-term financial forecast is, therefore, an important and integral part of the assessment of the movement of cash within the monthly period.

3   Overheads

INTRODUCTION

Overheads are those elements of cost which cannot be directly costed to individual projects and which are in effect indirect to the unit of production. Site overheads should, wherever possible, be costed to the project concerned and such items as site telephone, site light, heat and power, and the general foreman's salary, can be allocated without difficulty.

Overheads in the construction industry usually arise under the following subdivisions:

- production
- administration
- marketing and selling
- development and research (in the case of larger companies)

The allocation and costing of overheads in these categories is discussed in Chapter 9.

Overheads could also be classified on the basis of those which are fixed and do not, therefore, vary with turnover, and those which are variable.

OVERHEAD BUDGET

To effectively manage and financially control a building company it is essential to prepare an overhead budget at the start of the company's financial year. The budget should be analysed under various cost centres and actual costs monitored against estimated costs on a monthly basis. Normally budgets will include:

- overheads for the last financial year
- budget for the current financial year
- budget to date (each calendar month)

- actual cost to date (each calendar month)

The budget can either be prepared using previous records which are updated for inflation and known or anticipated changes in circumstances, or alternatively it can be calculated from first principles. Whichever method is adopted, once the budget has been completed a quick appraisal will usually reveal that the majority of individual items are relatively fixed and cannot easily be reduced. Only a few items will be controllable to any significant extent.

ANALYSIS OF TYPICAL OVERHEADS

It would be useful to analyse the overheads that would form part of the overhead budget for a typical medium-sized contractor/developer. Obviously the level of control that can be exercised by management will vary considerably and, consequently, so will the related impact on profitability. Individual senior members of staff will usually be made responsible for certain aspects of overheads within their sphere of operation, although the directors of the company will primarily be responsible for this aspect of cost.

OFFICES

The offices used by the administrative staff, including possibly a yard, stores and plant department, will give rise to certain overheads that are virtually fixed and have no direct relationship with turnover. These will include:

- rent – paid to the owner of the premises if they are leased
- loan interest – if the offices and yard are owned by the company but mortgaged
- rates
- lighting and heating
- repairs to premises and building upkeep – will include minor repairs (not capitalised) redecoration, office cleaning, etc. This can be a significant item, but if times are hard, cost cuttings can be achieved by delaying or cancelling the work

OFFICE EXPENSES
The day-to-day expenses in running the office are, to some extent, more

directly linked with turnover (except perhaps those associated with tendering), and will include printing and stationery, telephone, and postage.

Printing and stationery

This item can often reach significant proportions which will warrant management allocating specific responsibility for its cost. Representatives can sometimes be very persuasive and encourage over-ordering to an excessive extent. When documents such as letter-heads, order forms, invoices or payment cetificates are to be printed, care should be taken in the design in order to avoid frequent changes. The amount of printed format ordered and the stock levels maintained should be agreed by management. Often the most expensive single item in this category will be for photocopying and again some management control may be essential. The purchase of office equipment will normally be capitalised but charges for repairs and maintenance of typewriters, computers and business and accounting machines will probably be included under this grouping.

Telephone

Telephone bills can be a very significant item, particularly when a substantial part of the management role is communication with the site, suppliers and sub-contractors. Builders often operate over wide geographical areas, well outside local call rating. Many essential calls will be made Monday to Friday between 9 am and 1 pm at the peak rate charge and almost all of the remainder at the standard rate charge, 8 am to 9 am and 1 pm to 6 pm.

In order to illustrate costs, at the time of going to print, local calls at peak rate cost £3.04 per hour and at standard rate £2.02 per hour; calls up to 35 miles at peak rate cost £8.05 per hour and at standard rate £5.98 per hour; and calls over 35 miles at peak rate cost £10.12 per hour and at standard rate £8.05 per hour. Calls over certain low cost routes are slightly cheaper. At an average cost of £7.07 per hour, if each member of staff were to use the telephone for half an hour per day for 48 weeks of the year, this would cost approximately £850 per annum. Obviously, some members of staff have an aversion to the telephone, whilst others have no comprehension of its relentless addition to cost. The policy of restricting the use of the telephone to business calls only, and encouraging its use after 1 pm, will be cost-effective but may restrict business efficiency, and cause staff irritation. A more flexible approach will probably have to be followed, provided this is not abused by staff.

Postage

Other than grading correspondence and payments first or second class, there is little that can be done to control costs. One useful point is to ensure that all correspondence for posting is accumulated centrally and sorted so that letters, cheques, orders, etc., for the same address are sent in one envelope wherever possible. Development companies with a legal department may decide to use the British Document exchange. This is an organisation which guarantees next day delivery to those firms and organisations who pay an annual subscription; these include most solicitors, some building societies, local authorities, etc. Post is collected from a central point in a city or town, transferred to London for sorting, and returned to the respective collecting points the next day. The system is reliable and widely used.

MOTOR EXPENSES

Where it is policy to provide company cars for directors, senior management, surveyors and contract managers, the number of cars owned or leased by a builder is likely to be high in comparison with many other types of business. Due to the nature of the industry, unless administrative staff are site-based, extensive travelling costs will be incurred, whether paid as expenses or by transport provided. Various organisations produce detailed analyses from time to time of the annual running costs of motor cars of varying engine capacity. A simple assessment can be made on the basis of:

- Standing charges – say £260 per vehicle to cover such items as road fund tax and insurance (unless accounted for separately). It should be noted that insurance rates for company vehicles tend to be higher than those for privately owned vehicles, and are usually related to the previous year's claims.
- Running costs – petrol, oil, tyres and general repairs will amount to, say, 13p per mile. Obviously actual costs will vary between vehicles and depend not only on engine capacity but also to some extent on the average age of the car fleet.

Business mileages of 10000 to 15000 per annum are common in the building industry, which will therefore result in an approximate cost per vehicle of £1 560 to £2 210 respectively. These costs of course exclude the initial purchase cost, interest and depreciation. An alternative to purchasing a company car fleet would be leasing, and management will need to make a careful assessment regarding the merits and financial advantages of these options.

Company cars often represent part of a salary package to employees and from the staff viewpoint can be a considerable benefit. The use of a company car is now, however, subject to an income tax assessment as a benefit.

Management must ensure that the staff make efficient use of their time and wherever possible restrict unnecessary journeys. Junior members of staff can often be over-enthusiastic about site visits and take every opportunity to be away from the office. A cynic once said of a member of staff who had clocked up a mileage of 30 000 in a year, that if he worked eight hours a day, five days a week, for 48 weeks, out of a possible working year of 1 920 hours at an average speed of 30 miles an hour, he had spent 1 000 hrs over six months in his car.

TRAVELLING EXPENSES AND SUBSISTENCE

Travelling expenses will be paid to those members of staff using their own vehicles for company business. Some companies may utilise the local authority approach of a different rate for essential users and casual users, but more commonly a standard rate per mile is adopted. An alternative method is to pay a fixed annual sum for travelling expenses. This may particularly apply to firemen and other site-based staff. From the employee's point of view, most companies pay less than is strictly required to offset all the capital and running costs of keeping a car on the road, and pay well below the recognised rates used by the AA, local authority or similar bodies.

Where staff use public transport and are required to be absent from home overnight, subsistence payments will be made. Where such payments relate to a specific project, the cost may be allocated direct rather than charged to overheads.

It is possible that lunches and other forms of entertainment could be included under this heading, although most companies keep a fairly strict control over undue expenditure in this area.

INSURANCES

Insurances are a significant item and can represent a considerable expense in the overhead budget.

FIRE INSURANCE

All buildings and property owned by the builder should be insured against fire and the policy will normally include such aspects as theft, and damage resulting from storm or flood, riot or civil commotion, aircraft, subsidence or ground heave, escape of water or frost damage, and impact from vehicles or falling trees. When properties are mortgaged, the mortgagee will usually take out the insurance, but the builder will be required to pay the premiums. When properties are not mortgaged or used as security for bank borrowing, provision of fire insurance is at the discretion of the company. Often estimates of replacement cost of buildings are unrealistically low and as a result property is under-insured.

Contents of buildings will normally be included in the policy and again, care should be taken with the valuation.

Fire insurance premiums relating to individual contracts or development will be charged direct to the job concerned.

MOTOR INSURANCE

Staff in the building industry often reach mileages in excess of 15 000 a year on company business and, together with high mileages recorded for vans and lorries, this is likely to result in a greater incidence of accidents than the national average. As a result insurance companies tend to charge higher than average premiums. When the builder has a large fleet of vehicles the premiums are often related to claims made in earlier years.

PUBLIC AND EMPLOYER'S LIABILITY INSURANCE

This is an essential insurance to indemnify the builder against any claims arising from the damage to property or persons as a result of building operations or other activities of the company. The insurance will normally cover injury to any person and damage to property other than property belonging to the insured, property in his custody or control, or property in the custody or control of any employee.

CONTRACTOR'S ALL RISK

This form of insurance is intended to provide all risk cover in respect of both temporary and permanent works while in course of construction and until handed over to the client. Cover will also apply during the maintenance period, and will include unfixed materials and equipment, plant equipment, tools, temporary buidings and possibly employees' tools. The small print must be read carefully, particularly regarding the amount of any excess and limitations relating to damage to existing property in which or on which the builder may be working.

CITB LEVY

See Chapter 6.

APPRENTICES AND TRAINING

Costs will only arise under this heading when it would be improper to charge indirect labour costs or expenses associated with training to the respective project where the operative was working when the costs were incurred.

ADVERTISING

Costs may arise where advertisements are placed to recruit staff, promote the general services provided by the company or advertise the whole of the company's development programme. Specific advertisements relating to the sale of houses or commercial or industrial units on a particular development would normally be costed to the development concerned.

LEGAL AND ARCHITECTURAL EXPENSES

Legal or architectural expenses arising from specific projects which have already commenced, or are likely to, should be costed direct to the scheme concerned. Legal expenses which cannot be specifically allocated to a cost centre will be charged to the overhead accounts, together with legal or architectural expenses for abortive schemes. Equally, when architectural expenses and planning fees are incurred on sites owned by the company but planning permission is not obtained, land values remain unchanged and the cost concerned should be charged to overheads and written off in the current financial year.

SUBSCRIPTIONS

Subscriptions to charities or political parties will form part of the overheads but such costs are obviously avoidable and entirely at the discretion of the directors.

DEPRECIATION

Depreciation is the exhaustion of the effective life of a fixed asset due to its use or obsolesence. A charge must therefore be made each year against profits to cover the estimated amounts by which the value of the assets has deteriorated in the current financial year.

The method used must be stated in the notes on the accounts. Most builders adopt the reducing balance method, utilising percentages designed to write off the cost of equipment, plant, vehicles, etc., over the period of their use. By using a fixed percentage, early years are charged with the largest amounts for depreciation, the asset is never completely written off and some charge is made to revenue each year; the method is very simple to operate. The percentage rate used will vary depending upon the estimated life of the fixed asset concerned. There is also an advantage in the equalisation of cost for plant repairs in that when plant and equipment is new the depreciation will be high and the maintenance cost low, whereas when plant is nearing the end of its useful life depreciation will be low and maintenance costs higher.

A second method of providing for depreciation is the fixed instalment or straight line method. In this case a fixed percentage of the original cost of the asset is written off each year, thus ultimately reducing the value to nil. It is important to classify the life of different types of plant and equipment in order that they are written off over the period of their estimated effective life. The prudence concept must prevail, and over-optimistic life spans avoided.

Other ways of providing for depreciation include the annuity method, the depreciation fund with investment method, the depreciation fund with insurance method, and the working hours method.

One factor worth noting is that maintenance and repairs to plant and equipment should normally be charged to revenue and written off against profits in the current year and *not* capitalised.

Typical notes included in the company accounts would be:

Depreciation on plant and equipment has been provided by the straight line and reducing balance methods, using percentages designed to write off the cost of the equipment over the estimated period of its use. Percentages used are as follows:

	Percentage per annum
Freehold and long leasehold buildings	1 – 5
Fixed plant, furniture and fittings	10 – 25
Construction plant	10 – 33
Motor vehicles	20 – 25

Leases with less than 50 years unexpired are written off over their remaining lives.

BANK INTEREST AND CHARGES, LOAN INTEREST AND HIRE PURCHASE INTEREST

These items are discussed in detail in Chapter 2.

For many builders, particularly those involved with development, this will be the most singificant item of overhead cost. Unless interest rates are fixed, which would be unusual, interest represents the most volatile and unpredictable overhead expense. Sudden changes in world affairs or government policy can have a dramatic impact on interest rates. Moreover, with residential development, all too often when interest rates are rising demand for housing falls, thus leaving the developer in the straightjacket of rising overhead costs and reduced or delayed income.

AUDITOR'S REMUNERATION

As invoiced by the auditor!

DIRECTORS' FEES AND SALARIES

The emoluments of the chairman and directors must be shown separately in the financial accounts. It is required that the salary of the chairman of the board should be shown, the salary of the highest paid director, and the salaries of other directors in bands of nil to £5000 (£5001 to £10000, £10001 to £15000, etc.). The names of the directors who serve during the year and the beneficial and family interests of those serving at the end of the year, in shares and debentures of the company, must also be disclosed.

STAFF SALARIES

Staff salaries and associated costs, such as national insurance, will form part of the overheads. Some companies may allocate a proportion, or indeed most of the staff salaries to the cost accounts and they will then form part of the work in progress in the financial accounts. Companies must provide details in the notes to the accounts of the average number of persons employed, including the cost incurred in respect of wages and salaries, social security cost and other pension costs. Emoluments to senior staff must also be disclosed when these exceed £30000 per annum, and the number of staff stated in bands of £5000. For the majority of building companies, staff salaries and associated costs represent a significant part of the overheads.

INDIRECT LABOUR

Costs resulting from such situations as time wasted between jobs, and weather conditions preventing any work on site (for example in periods of continuous frost) will wherever possible be allocated to specific projects. Where this proves impossible it may be more appropriate that such costs are included with the general overheads.

DEPARTMENTAL PROFITS

It is probable that in most companies departmental profits may arise to offset overheads. In larger companies, departments such as plant and transport may be isolated and formed into separate companies in order that performance and responsibility can be clearly identified and monitored.

PLANT

If a plant department is efficiently managed and all items of plant are correctly and regularly costed to individual projects, it should be possible to achieve an internal profit on the use of company's plant. When contract managers and foremen are expected to use internal plant, it is vital that it is well maintained, in good working order, and that a comparable delivery and maintenance service is provided to that obtained from external plant hire companies. It is also perhaps a useful incentive to offer a discount of, say, 10% on the prevailing external hire rates to encourage the maximum use of company plant. Where internal plant is sub-standard, contract managers will endeavour to short-circuit the system and hire externally.

Plant can be divided into categories:

* mechanical plant
* mechanical plant with a skilled driver
* non-mechanical plant
* small tools

The company should set a standard daily or weekly hire rate for each item of plant, and individual projects should be costed, and the plant department credited, for the period it is used.

The total cost of small tools is frequently charged to the site and credited in part if they are returned in good condition.

The paper income or internal transfer received from the plant hire will be offset by the direct costs of running the plant department, including interest on capital, depreciation, maintenance and repair costs and the plant department staff. Provided the plant owned by the company is internally hired for a substantial percentage of the year and its use therefore credited to the plant department, a profit should be achieved.

In ideal circumstances a company will endeavour to keep all its own plant in constant use and utilise externally hired plant to meet any temporary excess need, thus avoiding standing or idle costs.

OWN TRANSPORT

The company's commercial transport, vans and lorries, may be included within the orbit of the plant department or granted a separate identity.

It is difficult to manage small works or indeed the company's own plant department without company transport. It may, however, prove difficult to achieve an efficient and profitable use and it is likely that some vehicles will be under-utilised. Frequently company transport may be co-opted to resolve a crisis on site caused by bad management and in any event the ready availability of a lorry and driver can lead to carelessness on the part of management in, for example, material deliveries.

Unless high rates are charged the returns for hiring out company transport to sites, less all the associated running costs, may in the final analysis only provide a marginal profit.

OWN STORES

The majority of large companies try to avoid the maintenance of stores, and utilise local builders' merchants as a more viable alternative. However, where companies maintain a stores department it is vital that it is managed with efficiency, cost-effectiveness and with supporting internal documentation.

Provided the percentage on costs is high enough to offset running costs, stores issue is monitored and documented, and theft, waste, double-handling and stock loss kept to negligible proportions, an internal profit should be achieved.

Efficient management is vital to:

- Calculate shelf turnover, stock levels and number of lines to be stocked.
- Control the return of surplus materials from the site and assess the viability of accepting them into the stores yard. Alternatively, surplus materials should be returned to the merchant (with acceptance of a restocking charge of, say, 15%) or scrapped.
- Arrange clearance sales of any surplus materials as necessary.
- Make efficient use of available space and design suitable storage and racking with sufficient circulation space to permit the use of pallets and a fork-lift truck.

RENTS RECEIVED

Many companies own property or land for which rents are receivable. It is sometimes possible to undertake commercial development for offices or factories and arrange long-term finances where A1 tenants have signed long leases. In such circumstances the rents received may offset the interest paid and the company may gain the advantage of any capital growth.

INTEREST RECEIVED

Where a company is not operating on an overdraft or other funding but has cash surpluses it will be possible to invest such funds to provide a return to the company. Even where cash surpluses are only available for short periods it is possible to place money on overnight deposit and earn interest. The company in any event may have invested money on a long-term basis irrespective of day-to-day needs.

When a company is involved in speculative development and house sales are managed within the company through a sales and legal department, house reservation fees and deposits on exchange of contracts will be kept in an interest-bearing client account.

CASH DISCOUNT

Cash discounts are not usually deducted from invoices before costing and therefore accumulate in a separate ledger account in the financial accounts.

Not all merchants offer cash discounts but as an approximate guide it could be assumed that the cash discount of $2\frac{1}{2}\%$ accruing on materials, external plant hire and nominated sub-contractors, and 5% on nominated suppliers will apply to approximately 50% of all expenditure. A turnover of £10m per annum will therefore result in an approximate cash discount of £125 000.

4 Estimating and Tendering Procedures

INTRODUCTION

There are numerous books on estimating practice and on the various methods of obtaining tenders which include open tendering, selective tendering, serial tendering, negotiated contracts, cost plus contracts, management fee contracts, package-deal contracts and design and build contracts. Many of these books are written from the viewpoint of the client and state that the objective of tendering is to give the client the building he wants, when he wants it, and at an optimum economic price.

The architect, whether he is employed by the client or builder, may, or indeed may not, give the client the building he wants. All too often architects design the building that *they* want, that the planning authority wants, or that the community wants. The client *may* get the building when he wants it, but so often design preparation and the planning and building regulation approval process absorb all the time and the client's patience. Achieving an optimum economic price is no simple matter as buildability, time and quality will all influence the final cost to both the builder and the client.

There is a tendency for the client's needs to be met more fully, when the architect and builder are working together in close harmony and both are listening to and understanding the other's point of view. This is most often demonstrated when private housing development schemes are built to time, quality and cost, with good design and in harmony with the environment. Moreover, in recent years, many builders have grasped the opportunity and with true entrepreneurial spirit have developed expertise and service to the client with design and build package-deal solutions to construction problems.

When preparing estimates and tenders for building work, there is a substantial difference in procedure depending on whether the estimate is for small works, contracting, or housing and industrial development.

TENDERING FOR SMALL WORKS

Tendering for small works is a specialist area and the estimator/surveyor must have wide experience and a detailed knowledge of construction methods and the labour and material costs likely to be incurred. Normally the client will only supply the drawings and specification, and the estimator will need to take off approximate quantities and spot items for pricing. Often omnibus rates will be used and individual rates will only be built up for items with large quantities. The oncosts and overheads on small works will be high and the estimator will include between 25% and 100% to cover such costs. The real problem in pricing or estimating for small works is the propensity for additional costs to be incurred because:

- The quantities of materials used are small and therefore more difficult to obtain.
- Small loads are often surcharged by manufacturers delivering direct, or, when purchased from a builders' merchant's yard, sold at an enhanced rate to cover overheads and double-handling.
- Skilled labour is often less enthusiastic about small works than about housing or larger contracts, usually because it is more difficult to earn good bonuses where operatives are directly employed; in the case of sub-contractors, it is hard for them to achieve a good financial return even at very enhanced rates.
- Continuity of labour either within the project or between projects is difficult to achieve and needs excellent management input to control, particularly where the work may only last for a few hours.

As a result the real cost for different builders undertaking small works may vary dramatically. The lowest cost will usually be achieved by those firms whose labour is skilled in several trades and who are therefore able to maintain improved continuity. The client, therefore, when obtaining say four quotations for a small project, may be surprised to see a spread of tenders varying by up to 100%.

The estimate to the client, often in the form of a letter, should clearly specify the work included, the terms of payment, and how variations are to be dealt with. Some companies use standard forms prepared by the Building Employers Confederation.

Invariably with small works most disputes with clients stem from what was or was not included in the estimate. For example, in a simple situation where two rooms with solid floors are converted into one, the estimator may have included an item for making good the floor finish. If as is often the case there is an excessive difference in floor levels, it may be necessary to relay a large percentage of the floor screed. The builder will inevitably treat such an item as a variation. Similarly, clients often give instruction to workmen on site regarding such items as additional power points without enquiring of the builder the cost implication. It follows that for a good working relationship with the client, the estimator should set out clearly, in plain English, exactly what is included in the estimate and, if thought prudent, include provisional sums for items where the extent of work is in doubt.

TENDERING FOR CONTRACTS

Design and build and package-deal contracts, together with housing and industrial development, are discussed later in the chapter.

The builder's first problem is to identify opportunities to submit tenders for work. To this end it is important to publicise the company and its capacity and expertise to as wide a circle of potential clients as possible in the geographical area in which it is desired to work. This may be by:

- Letter to architects and other potential clients.
- Personal visits to clients and architects by the directors or other senior members of staff.
- Advertisements in *Yellow Pages* and the national or local trade press.
- Checking planning application lists, trade press and local press for details of forthcoming projects and writing to ask to be included on the list of tenderers.
- Arranging press releases or other articles in the local or trade press when projects have just started or have been completed.
- Extensive use of site publicity including well designed and expertly sign-written site boards.

It may be useful, if the company is large enough, to prepare a brochure with photographs and details of prestigious work undertaken by the company over, say, a five-year period. Some national or public companies provide information of this nature as part of the annual financial accounts and indeed, in some cases, such material may form from 50% to 75% of the whole.

OPEN TENDERING

Builders, if short of work, may be tempted to respond to advertisements inviting tenders for a project. The problem with open and indiscriminate tendering of this nature is that builders may respond who are both financially and practically unsound. Not only is their price likely to be too low, but they are unlikely to be capable of providing a good performance. Although the client does not bind himself to accept the lowest, or indeed *any*, tender, the temptation to accept the lowest may be overwhelming.

Competition for the average builder, therefore, unless there is a boom period and tendering is restricted, is likely to be severe, with perhaps 15 to 20 firms submitting a genuine price. In such circumstances the probability of obtaining the job, or of obtaining the job at a reasonable price, is very slim and probably not worth the expense and effort involved.

SELECTIVE TENDERING

The more satisfactory method is set out in the *Code of Procedure for Single Stage Selective Tendering* 1977 which states that:

'Once it has been decided that a contractor is to be selected by competitive tender, a short list of suitable tenderers should be drawn up either from the employer's approved list of contractors or from an *ad hoc* list of contractors of established skill, integrity, responsibility and proven competence for work of the character and size contemplated. It should be appreciated that because of the cost of preparing tenders the larger the tender lists become the greater will be the cost of abortive tendering, and this must be reflected in building prices.'

To this end a selective tender list should vary between a maximum of five to eight tenders, depending on the size of the contract.

Sometimes advertisements are placed in the local, national or technical press providing details of a proposed project and inviting builders to apply to be placed on a selective tendering list. When the client is considering whether or not to place a builder on the list, the following factors will be taken into account:

- the company's financial standing and past record
- whether the firm has had recent experience of building at the required output over a comparable contract period

- the company's general experience and reputation for the type of work envisaged, and whether the management structure of the company is adequate
- whether the company will have adequate capacity at the relevant time

To some extent for many builders this is a chicken and egg situation in that they are unable to demonstrate a track record without being given the opportunity to build up experience.

PRICING BILLS OF QUANTITIES

Whether tenders are being submitted under the open or selective method, bills of quantities are often, but not invariably, provided by the client. Usually bills are prepared in accordance with the Standard Method of Measurement of Building Works. Unless specifically stated in the bill the SMM provides that the following shall be deemed to be included with all items:

'(a) Labour and all costs in connection therewith.
(b) Materials, goods, and all costs in connection therewith.
(c) Fitting and fixing materials and goods in position.
(d) Plant and all costs in connection therewith.
(e) Waste of materials.
(f) Square cutting.
(g) Establishment charges, overhead charges and profit.'

In reality this will break down to:

- labour, whether directly employed or sub-contract
- materials and waste
- plant
- overheads and profit

The builder's estimator will generally be responsible for pricing the bill of quantities although perhaps the preliminaries and certain specific items, such as profit and attendance on nominated sub-contractors, may be the prerogative of management, when the tender is finalised.

LABOUR

Pricing is a life-long study for most estimators, and although labour constants in such publications as *Spon's* or *Griffiths* may have been used as a base, feedback from site or information produced by work study will have been absorbed and assimilated to develop the estimator's own schedule of constants.

In essence the constants represent the estimated time to complete a unit of production, allowing for tea and other breaks, inclement weather, site conditions, time spent receiving instructions and understanding design requirements, delays locating materials and plant, boredom, improved output when work is repetitive, and interrelation with other trades or operatives.

The all-in hourly rate for operatives, whether skilled, semi-skilled or labourers, will be calculated periodically or adopted from other published sources, and will include all on-costs such as national insurance contributions, holiday with pay schemes, allowances to cover sick pay, redundancy, CITB levy and employer's liability insurance. In order to average out these on-costs the computation will be made by calculating the number of productive hours worked in a year and dividing the result into the total annual cost to produce the hourly rate.

The labour element of some items in the bill of quantities such as bricklaying or concreting is more easily dealt with using a rate for a gang rather than for an individual operative.

Where, as is common, labour-only sub-contractors are extensively used, the estimator has a choice of pricing either using constants and hourly rates, as for directly employed labour, or substituting labour-only sub-contract rates and associated on-costs. More commonly the former approach will be adopted and the builder's surveyor will be left with the calculation of the difference between the cost target and labour-only sub-contract rate.

When work within a company is traditionally sub-let to a labour and material sub-contractor, such as plumbing, electrical work or plastering, estimates will be obtained from the specialist sub-contractor, a percentage added for on-costs, and the respective rates inserted in the bill of quantities.

When determining an adjustment to standard constants for items of work in the bill, the estimator will take into account the quality and quantity of the work, the degree of repetitiveness and familiarity of the firm's operatives with the type of work, and an assessment of buildability (whether the work is complex and intricate or straightforward).

The estimator should also visit the site, inspect the contract drawings and liaise with contract management in order to adjust constants to take account of site conditions, the time of year when different parts of the building will be constructed and the pre-tender construction programme.

To some extent the size of the company will determine the level of sophistication achieved in amending constants to take account of the individual circumstances of each tender. The management of some smaller companies may prefer that the estimator prices the bill on a standard basis and that the directors or senior management responsible for tender adjudication and submission make the necessary adjustments.

MATERIALS AND WASTE

The first job of the estimator on receipt of the bill of quantities is to send out enquiries to suppliers in order to ascertain the materials cost. Normally not more than three suppliers or sub-contractors would be asked to quote and it is often good practice to utilise photocopied extracts from the bill of quantities, including associated preambles, to ensure that no misunderstandings occur.

In assessing the basic cost of materials, allowance must be made for:

- waste, including breakages and vandalism
- unloading and storage
- any shrinkage and consolidation
- packaging, crates, pallets and any transport costs
- fixings such as nails and screws
- any additional costs for small quantities
- increased costs when the quotation is for a limited period
- any potential delays in delivery which may affect the contract programme
- cash and trade discount or rebates

PLANT

Mechanical and non-mechanical plant will either be priced in individual items in the bill or in the preliminaries. For larger contracts the pre-tender programme should outline plant utilisation and the length of time each item of plant will be needed on site. When the company's own plant is used the operating cost of mechanical plant should be calculated, including both the standing and running costs. Where plant is hired externally running costs should also be included. As with labour constants plant constants included in the build-up of the rate must take account of the site conditions, the time of year, the quantity of work and whether output will be continuous or intermittent. For some items of plant, particularly excavating equipment, the skill of the driver will also make a significant contribution to output.

Where items of plant such as scaffolding, cranes, hoists, concrete mixers and dumpers are being used by several trades or operatives at the same time, it will probably be preferable to price such items in the preliminaries.

OVERHEADS AND PROFIT

A percentage to cover overheads and profit may either be added to each rate in the bill included in the preliminaries or added on the final summary page, depending on company policy.

BUILD-UP OF RATES

The measured items in the bill of quantities will be priced by building up each rate from the constituent elements, labour, materials, plant, overheads and profit. It is helpful if each element can be separately identified in order that a priced breakdown can be provided for the buying department and management when tenders have been successful.

Some companies use computers for estimating and programs have been developed which are simple to use and very efficient in operation. Labour and plant constants can be built into the program and current labour and material prices input for each tender. Where trades or elements are required to be executed under different circumstances than were envisaged when the constants were built into the program, it should be possible to amend them by a factor such as 0.9 or 1.1 to take account of the prevailing circumstances.

When the pricing of individual items in the bill has been completed, including attendance and profit on nominated sub-contractors, the bill should be extended and totalled. It is at this stage that errors frequently occur, and the entry of rates from work schedules to the bill and extending and totalling should all be checked.

SITE OVERHEADS/PRELIMINARIES

The pricing of the preliminaries will either be undertaken by estimator or by management. The most significant items to be included in the preliminaries will comprise:

- Site staff – site manager/agent or general foreman and other site-based staff whose emoluments are not included in the rates. On large projects this may well include site engineers, surveyors, clerks and other staff who in smaller companies would be part of the general overheads.
- Scaffolding – both external and internal.
- Site huts, and ancillary storage facilities and toilets.
- Mechanical plant – not included in individual rates.
- Small tools and sundry non-mechanical plant.
- Maintenance costs and remedial work arising under defects liability.
- Temporary roads and fencing.
- Temporary water, electricity and telephone services.
- Safety, welfare and first aid.
- Insurances, including public and employer's liability.
- For fixed price contracts, an allowance for increased costs.

Examination of the priced bills of many builders will reveal that usually the majority of preliminary items are left unpriced and the monetary value is concentrated in a few significant items. Some firms include some or all of their profit in the preliminaries, allocating it to a neutral and secure item unaffected by variations, such as site huts, plant or site services.

In any event, at tender adjudication any changes made to the priced bills will usually be adjusted by adding or subtracting from the value of the preliminaries. The detailed pricing therefore often bears little relationship to real cost.

ESTIMATOR'S REPORT

On completion of the pricing of the bills of quantities the estimator will normally provide a written report to the management responsible for tender adjudication. In smaller companies the estimator may give a verbal report based on his notes. The report should contain certain key facts relating to the estimate, and include:

- Value of the builder's own work, excluding labour and material sub-contractors. This should be sub-divided into directly employed labour, labour-only sub-contractors, materials and plant included in the rates.
- Value of labour and material sub-contractors.
- Value of prime cost and provisional sums including total of profit and attendance.
- A list of provisional sums and contingencies.

- Cash discount on materials, labour and material sub-contractors, nominated sub-contractors and suppliers.
- A complete breakdown of preliminaries.
- Profit.
- A list of any suspected errors or omissions in the bill of quantities.
- A list of any problems revealed by the site visit and inspection of the architect's drawing, including if possible an indication of the state of readiness of the architect in the completion of the working drawings and progress with regard to nominations.
- An indication of any unusual work or construction methods and possible material delivery delays.

TENDER ADJUDICATION

Once the estimator has completed the pricing of the bills it is the role of management to finalise the tender. This adjudication may be at a formal board meeting or by a select group of directors and senior management with specific responsibility for tendering. In some companies one director may be responsible for the majority of tenders and only those over a certain value would receive wider consideration by management.

Tendering is a skilful task; it requires keen attention to detail and a finely tuned awareness of market conditions. All too often builders panic and submit too low a price in order to maintain turnover. Profits on contracting are frequently marginal and great care must be exercised when finalising tenders.

During the adjudication process management should give consideration to the following factors in arriving at the tender figure.

WORK IN HAND

The level of the company's workload will, to a large extent, govern the attitude of management to an individual tender. Most companies produce each month, as part of their management accounts, an assessment of workload for a period of 12 to 18 months ahead. This may be presented in a calculated or graphical format and will usually show a declining workload over the period. When the work in hand is declining rapidly, management may be tempted to cut tenders to maintain workload.

TENDERS IN HAND

An assessment should be made of tenders in hand each month, again as part of the management accounts. The proforma should indicate the approximate contract value of each tender, the range of competition (if known), site location, and an assessment on, say, a scale of 10, of the priority of management to secure one contract in preference to another.

AVAILABILITY OF STAFF

A schedule should be available of all site staff, their specialist and technical knowledge, capability and previous experience, and date of availability or release from existing commitments.

PROFITABILITY

The estimator's report will provide an assessment of the expected profit to be achieved if the tender is successful. The profit will of course be dependent to some extent on the relationship between turnover (work in hand) and overheads. In very simple terms, if the normal turnover of the company, taking one year with another had been £2m per annum, overheads £160 000 and gross profit £200 000 (10%), the net profit for the year would be £40,000 (2%) and overheads would be 8%.

If in the current year, however, the projected turnover for the next 12 months was £1½m, overheads were static at £160 000 and profit levels remained at 10%, the company would make a loss of £10 000 and overheads would represent 10.67% of projected turnover. A successful tender with 10% added for overheads and profit, which would generate £½m turnover in the next 12 months would restore the company's financial position to normal.

In certain circumstances management may decide to cut the margin for overheads and profit. A reduction to, say, 5% would generate a gross profit of £25 000 and, together with the 10% profit on the remainder of the turnover, less overheads, would leave a net profit of £15 000. Even at a profit level of 2% on the tender the company would break even during the year. Such a policy is obviously only a short-term expediency to overcome the immediate problem but it does provide a contribution towards overhead costs and although the individual project will make a net loss the company as a whole will remain profitable.

It should of course be appreciated that although profit margins on contracts assessed as a percentage against turnover are low in the construction industry, because interim payments are usually made by the client each month, the profit on capital invested will show a very different picture.

ABILITY OF ARCHITECT OR OTHER SUPERVISING OFFICER

It is common practice to "price", either in the form of a discount or surcharge, the ability (or lack of it) of the architect and other consultants involved in supervising a project. When a signficant proportion of the detailed design work remains uncompleted at tender stage this gives some indication that problems may develop. A decisive, fair-minded architect can aid the builder in achieving a good standard of work completed on time. On the other hand, lack of information, delays in decision-making and unfair fault-finding can frustrate and demoralise even the most conscientious of builders.

CONTRACT CONDITIONS

An assessment should be made of the conditions of contract, whether JCT 80 or other standard form, and any alterations that have been made should be taken into account. Attention should also be paid to any special conditions contained in the bill of quantities relating to the execution of the work, such as restrictions on access and working hours, completion in stages or phases, or problems relating to adjoining property.

SITE CONDITIONS

The estimator's site report should be studied and, if felt necessary, a second inspection made. Consideration should be given to the cost impact of:

- ground conditions
- water table
- depths of excavation
- accessibility and, in the immediate locality, road widths and turning space for materials deliveries
- demolition or site clearance, particularly basements and existing foundations
- risk of vandalism during the contract period
- cost of securing the site

CONSTRUCTION METHODS AND PROGRAMME

The larger the project, the more important it will become for management to have a clear idea of the most economic method of execution of the work and the plant requirements. The pre-tender construction programme will assist in the preparation of the method statement and the determination of the contract period to be inserted in the tender documents, if this has not been predetermined by the client.

MARKET CONDITIONS

The identity of other tenderers can be a useful guide in determining the final tender price. The number of tenderers, and estimate of their workload, their recent tendering performance, and their enthusiasm for the current tender, can all assist in tender adjudication. It is useful to maintain a record of all tenders submitted and the relative performance of competitors. When this is not available from the client or his representative it may be possible to construct the result from third parties.

Some companies monitor tender results using a computer in an attempt to predict the possible tendering patterns of their competitors.

Obviously the state of the market and the volume of work available both locally and nationally is a major factor in determining the level of competition.

CAPITAL REQUIRED

Although where regular monthly interim payments are made the capital required for contracts is low, nevertheless an assessment should be made taking account of investment in plant, level of retention and any back- or front-end loading (see p.234). Obviously where projects are front-end loaded contracts may not only be self-financing but may also contribute capital for other activities of the company. An assessment should also be made of the financial implications of any risks taken in the estimate.

THE TENDER FIGURE

Having taken account of all the above factors, management will increase or decrease the price produced by the estimator to arrive at a tender figure and the appropriate contract period, where it has not been predetermined by the client.

This will result in an adjustment to the priced bills which will usually be made by amending the value of the preliminaries. Alternatively an adjustment can be made on the final summary page of the bill either as a lump sum or as a percentage amendment to the measured rates.

Management may decide to submit a very keen price in order to maintain cashflow or contribute to overheads, as discussed earlier in this chapter.

Once the decision has been made the tender form will be completed and returned to the appropriate issuing office. Except in very special circumstances, and with the agreement of the builders concerned, a minimum of four working weeks should be allowed for the preparation of tenders. Inevitably the builder will be hard-pressed to meet tender deadlines and care must be taken to submit the documentation before the latest time for submission, which will usually be specified as a particular hour of a particular day. Tenders received after this time should not under any circumstances be opened (unless there is only one), and will be returned to the builder concerned.

In view of the expense and effort involved in the preparation of tenders, builders will be best advised to deliver them by hand wherever possible to avoid potential postal delays. Moreover it is advisable to obtain a signed receipt from a responsible, identifiable person in the issuing office confirming receipt of the tender envelope, and the time and date. On more than one occasion the author has been involved in situations where the post office (first class normal service) has failed to deliver tenders within the specified period and, perhaps even more frustrating, one occasion where a tender was delivered by hand to a local authority and a receipt obtained, but the tender was mislaid and the signature could not be identified.

From time to time builders may find it necessary to qualify the tender or to send a covering letter raising particular problems. Where such difficulties emerge at an early date the issuing authority or architect should be advised in order that other tenderers can be informed if necessary.

COVER PRICES

Although it is considered unethical, some builders, if they are over-whelmed with enquiries and perhaps have had a number of recent tenders accepted, may decide to withdraw from serious consideration of the project and stop the estimator pricing the bills. At worst the builder may not even open the tender documentation. The builder will then make enquiries of other firms tendering and take a cover or safe price from another firm which is actively tendering. The cover price given by this firm will of course be somewhat higher than its own actual tender price and no information will be provided which would enable competitors to secure the contract. The firm concerned will be unlikely to provide the cover price before tender adjudication and it will therefore be very close to the tender date. Occasionally circumstances arise where the majority of firms tendering have taken a cover price and this may prove embarrassing if the lowest tenderer withdraws because of errors in the bill and the second, third and even fourth are all covers.

This practice has developed, with no apparent benefit to participating builders, because architects or employers have on occasions given the impression that failure to submit a tender will prejudice future enquiries or that they resent the builder picking and choosing the projects for which tenders are submitted.

Obviously in times of recession and shortage of work most builders will be actively tendering and therefore not participating in such practice. From a moral viewpoint the concept should be condemned and the author has never given or received cover prices.

It is obviously also possible that if the tenderers were all known to each other and so minded, a meeting could be arranged at which the tender price to be submitted could be agreed and either work shared or a monetary payment made by the lowest tenderer. In the author's experience such circumstances have never prevailed for main contracts but have possibly existed on occasion with materials suppliers. Rings such as these can be broken by obtaining quotations from firms well outside the immediate area of the site.

OPENING AND ACCEPTANCE OF TENDERS

It is of great benefit to the builder if tenders are opened as soon as possible after receipt and all the tenderers notified of the result. Sometimes only the lowest tenderer is advised and other builders do not even receive an acknowledgement even though they may have spent a considerable sum in preparing the tender. Unquestionably the best procedure from the builders' point of view is to be present when the tenders are opened. Once the lowest tender has been accepted other builders should be notified of the result through a list of all tenderers in alphabetical order and a list of tender prices in ascending order, with the accepted tender price and tenderer underlined. If names can be put to tender prices, this may be to the detriment of an individual builder in future competitions, as discussed earlier in the chapter.

It is also important that late tenders are not accepted by the client in any circumstances, as it is common practice for builders to exchange prices within a short period–often less than two hours after the closing time and date. A builders' merchant may sometimes act as an intermediary in this process.

The priced bills may be required to be submitted with the tender documentation but more commonly, and indeed more fairly for unsuccessful firms, in view of the work involved, are required to be submitted within a maximum period of four working days from a request advising that the tender is under consideration.

The bills will then be examined by the client's quantity surveyor to identify any errors, which will be adjusted in accordance with the terms of the tender documentation. If as a result of errors the lowest tender is withdrawn, the next lowest will be considered.

Frequently tenders remain open for acceptance for periods of up to three months, and the client is not bound to accept the lowest, or indeed any tender. Where the builder is not notified that a project has been abandoned until the period of acceptance has nearly expired it can cause severe problems with workload and forward planning. In the past this has often happened with local authority projects subject to economic policy decisions of central government.

ESTIMATING FOR HOUSING AND INDUSTRIAL DEVELOPMENT

Companies engaged in development may undertake their building work in three ways:

(a) Arrange for competitive tenders from other contractors.
(b) Negotiate a price for the work with the contracting division of the company or alternatively, obtain a tender from the contracting division but also arrange for tenders from other builders in order to monitor performance.
(c) Undertake the building work within the company or the development division of the company.

Where the building work is 'in house' and therefore not subject to external competition the builder will evolve procedures to arrive at estimated cost and the associated feasibility study.

TAKING OFF QUANTITIES

The working drawings of the development could be passed to a quantity surveyor for preparation of bills of quantities, ready for pricing by the builder, or by the quantity surveyor himself. More commonly the builder will arrange for his own surveyor to take off the quantities for the development.

From time to time one hears jokes concerning builders' quantities. In fact, however, such quantities are usually more accurate and of greater value than those produced by the client's quantity surveyor. The builder tendering on bills of quantities never has access to the original dimensions and is therefore obliged, if the tender is successful, to take off all the quantities a second time for buying, etc., thus introducing additional costs.

When taking off in house, the surveyor will ensure that the quantities can be used not only for estimating but also for buying, valuations and measurement of sub-contractors.

The method used will vary substantially from SMM6 and though a detailed analysis is outside the scope of this book, one example such as roof tiling is worth considering. A study of a roofing catalogue indicates that all basic taking off can be obtained from the technical data. The rafter length will govern the number of courses of tiles. For example, for Redland 49 interlocking tiles, rafter lengths of 4.039 to 4.267 linear metres requires 14 courses and 4.343 to 4.572 linear metres requires 15 courses.

When calculating the rafter length the surveyor will use the precise figure to determine the number of courses and double-check the calculation. The eaves length in linear metres will also indicate the number of tiles in each course. A simple calculation will therefore establish the exact number of tiles required except for any adjustment for chimneys etc.

The catalogue also indicates the battens required, i.e. 3.28 linear metres per metre squared at 305 mm gauge measured net. Waste calculations will also be made to arrive at actual buying quantities with separate labour items measured net.

The information so produced can therefore be used not only for estimating but also for materials purchasing and labour targets.

Where labour and material sub-contractors are to be used, drawings and specification notes may be sent out to tender and the taking off omitted.

PRICING

When the taking off and scheduling have been completed the documentation will be priced by the surveyor. The usual approach is to price the work net without allowance for overheads and profit and to keep the cost of materials, labour and plant distinct. The taking off and pricing will be kept separate for different sections of the work substructure, roads, footpaths, drainage, main sewers, and main services, together with a trade or elemental breakdown of individual housing or industrial units. This will be essential for both the preparation of the feasibility study and cost feedback and monitoring procedures.

FEASIBILITY STUDY

The feasibility study undertaken before site purchase is outlined in Chapter 7.

The exercise will be repeated before work commences on site with land costs and associated legal fees included and the expected profit representing the residual figure.

Detailed estimated costs as calculated above would be substituted for the approximate prices and prices per square metre used at the earlier stage.

Management will be concerned that accurate assessments are made of anticipated site and general overheads with particular reference to the projected cash flow and associated interest charges. It will also be necessary to discuss future trends in interest rates, potential market prices of the development and the rate of sale.

Management will meet, in a similar way to tender adjudication, to discuss the estimated costs and profit associated with development projects. The major difference is that the design itself, the cost implications of the design, buildability, site supervision and the contract period are all under the direct control of the builder. The uncertainties are concentrated in interest rates, sales and maintenance.

DESIGN AND BUILD

Increasingly clients are approaching one or several builders to obtain quotations for the complete building process, including design, specification and tender price. This concept of an 'all-in' service or package-deal is not new and is widely used overseas. The majority of publications are on balance sceptical of any advantages to the client and make such comments as, 'it is essential that the client's professional advisers check the design, both as regards suitability for its purpose, economy and structural stability'.

It is of course overlooked that a design and build contractor will only develop a good reputation by achieving an excellent design, suitable for its purpose, economical to build, maintain and use, and structurally stable. Photographs of completed projects will be included in brochures or in the financial accounts and potential clients are almost certain to make enquiries regarding past performance. Moreover, any design and build contractor of any standing will ensure that either he has on his staff the best available qualified architects, surveyors and other specialists who are sensitive to the requirements of the planners, good design, the client, the environment and building cost, or alternatively, engages the services of first class, independent architects and consultants.

Architects', quantity surveyors' and consultants' fees on large projects may amount to 12% of contract costs, while the builder's net profit may normally only be 2%. There is obviously some scope here for savings in cost from the builder's viewpoint (some part of which will almost certainly be passed on to the client), together with some distinct advantages:

- Specification and materials selection can be vetted by the buying department to avoid delays and achieve maximum savings in cost.
- Management will be involved early in the design process, thus ensuring that construction methods are both feasible and economic.
- New materials and construction methods may be pioneered.
- Taking off by the internal quantity surveyor will be freely available to staff and utilised for buying, measurement of sub-contractors and cost targets in a similar way to that described for housing development. This should represent a substantial saving in cost, as external bills of quantities state that the builder may only use them for ordering at his own risk and the original dimensions are not available. In effect therefore, the bill of quantities is of little value and not particularly cost-effective.
- Provided the client's brief to the builder is adequate and there has been proper consultation, including perhaps mock-ups or detailed models of the proposed building, there should be substantially fewer variation orders. In any event, because of the nature of a design and build project, the majority of variation orders and adjustments to the contract figure applicable to traditional contracts at final account stage will not apply, thus resulting in a substantial saving of resources. Variations to a

contract are often more expensive than the calculation arrived at using a traditional bill of quantities, and the cost of variations to the client for design and build contracts is therefore more likely to reflect actual cost.
- Supervision of the building work will be undertaken by the builder's own staff.

Some design and build contractors are prepared to put together a scheme for a client alongside the traditional approach using consultant architects and quantity surveyors. This may be a formidable challenge to the professionals, particularly when the builder may be able to produce the working drawings and completed tender in a fraction of the time taken using the traditional process.

On balance this approach to tendering, together with in-house development schemes for housing, offices and industrial properties, has made substantial inroads into the traditional approach. It must of course be emphasised that the professionals are still at work, but are simply employed direct by the contractor.

OTHER FORMS OF TENDERING AND CONTRACTUAL ARRANGEMENT

Circumstances can dictate that other forms of tendering and contractual arrangement are to the benefit of the client, builder, or indeed both, and this will apply to the whole spectrum of building work.

NEGOTIATED CONTRACT

The client may decide that his interests would best be served if a contract figure is negotiated direct with a particular builder. This situation may arise for a number of reasons.

Time

The project may be required to start immediately with insufficient tendering information, and be completed at the earliest possible date. This applies, for example, to shop conversions.

Business association

A relationship may have developed between a client and builder over a number of years. The builder may have proved that the company is able to produce high quality work, to time, and at a reasonable cost. The client may be aware that it would be possible to undercut the negotiated price but is nevertheless prepared to pay marginally extra for excellent service. Relationships of this type are common between builders and development companies and also where clients erect similar buildings country-wide, for example petrol stations.

Market conditions

When market conditions are deteriorating it is unlikely that a client would be prepared to negotiate. When the market is buoyant, however, and few if any builders are genuinely interested in a project, there will be extensive risk of a high incidence of covers. It may well then be in the client's interest to seek out a builder who would be prepared to negotiate.

SERIAL TENDERING

It is possible that the client may invite builders to tender for one project, for example a school, but advise each tenderer that the successful builder will be invited to negotiate for other schools at the same rates plus an allowance for increased costs. This can and does place the builder in a difficult position. For example, at the height of the school building programme in the early '70s it was common practice to split the construction programme of a local authority for a year into groups of 6 to 12 projects. Builders tendering were then placed in the invidious position of either turning down a substantial amount of work or, on the other hand, undertaking more work than they could comfortably manage. An advantage is that the client receives very competitive tenders and the builder does at least know his programme well ahead and can develop the expertise and resources to meet it. The next serial tender for the following year's programme, however, leaves the builder with an equally grave problem, particularly if expansion has been necessary to cope with the additional work load.

It is also possible that in the normal course of events and with no indication being given to the builder at the time of the original contract, a second contract or extension to an original contract will be negotiated on the basis of the original tender rates, to the mutual benefit of both parties.

Often negotiated contracts are based on earlier tenders and the rates in the original priced bill of quantities will form the basis of negotiation. Where there are no bills of quantities available, approximate priced quantities or a schedule of rates may be mutually agreed. Alternatively a form of prime cost contractual arrangement could be utilised.

COST PLUS CONTRACTS

As the name implies the builder receives payment for the total recorded cost of labour, materials, plant and sub-contractors' accounts, including ancillary costs, plus a percentage addition. The percentage addition could be negotiated or be subject to tender and would normally vary for each sub-heading with a larger percentage being applied to labour which is perhaps more directly related to management input.

MANAGEMENT FEE

An alternative to cost plus contracts is that a fixed management fee is paid to the builder for co-ordinating and managing the building project. The construction work may be carried out by the builder's own work force and domestic sub-contractors and all materials and plant supplied, which is in effect at cost plus a fixed fee. Alternatively the builder may merely act as co-ordinator and use the company's expertise to supervise and control the work which would be entirely carried out by independent sub-contractors. Each stage of the work can then be subject to competitive tenders. The builder could of course arrange to submit his own competitive tender for any particular stage.

This contractual approach can result in very economical construction, particularly if the builder is involved at the design stage. In certain circumstances other members of the construction team – quantity surveyors, architects, or engineers – may function in this co-ordination role but the builder is very well placed to be head of a management team with the resources and expertise of the company developed over many years.

TARGET COST CONTRACTS

In this case at the outset of a project the builder provides the client with an estimated cost including an allowance for overheads and profit (fee). It is agreed that any saving in actual cost will be divided between the builder and the client at an agreed percentage, usually 50:50. Alternatively a fee is agreed and a percentage of, say, 25% of any saving in cost is added to the fixed fee and 25% of any over-expenditure deducted.

COST AND COSTING

In each situation where the client is expected to pay the cost of a project the builder will need to take care to clearly demonstrate that:

- The cost system is accurate and all documentation is available for inspection.
- The materials have been obtained at competitive prices, unless urgently required.
- Waste has been kept to acceptable proportions. The client must be made aware that some element of waste will occur.
- Plant is only on site when needed.
- Labour is competitively employed either on a bonus scheme or sub-contract.
- Although some delays and management errors are inevitable, they have been kept within acceptable levels.

In any contract of this type it is essential that a good working relationship and degree of trust exists between the builder and the client.

SCHEDULE OF RATES

An alternative to tendering using a bill of quantities is that the builder is requested to price a comprehensive schedule of typical items for each trade to form a schedule of rates. Alternatively the client can supply the priced schedule and ask builders to quote on the basis of a percentage discount or surcharge to each trade or element. This form of tendering is more common for maintenance or rehabilitation contracts, where the quantity of work to be included in the contract is very uncertain.

Although the client can obtain competitive quotations, both the client and builder will be involved in an extensive remeasurement exercise and inevitably a substantial amount of negotiation throughout the period of the work. Moreover, neither party will be aware of the contract value.

COST TARGETS AND FEEDBACK

On completion of the estimating and tendering process, when the builder is awarded a contract the estimator will then be required to provide an analysis of the tender for management. In many companies this is simply not available.

In essence, whether the bill (internal or external) is priced manually or by computer, management will require a breakdown of each rate into its component parts – labour, material, plant, and overheads and profit. This breakdown will form the target or budget cost for various sections of the company and in due course actual costs can be compared and fed back to management to assist with the identification of profit or loss centres. This procedure is a useful and indeed essential part of the cost value reconciliation process, as a second check on figures produced by comparing overall cost with valuation with work in progress, as discussed later in Chapter 11.

5 Buying

INTRODUCTION

The buying process is often neglected by builders, who do not co-ordinate or centralise their materials purchasing, and as a consequence purchasing power is dissipated. Moreover, buying may be undertaken by junior, inexperienced staff or site management outside the discipline and control of a buying department, which may result in increased costs.

It should be appreciated that more than 50% of the cost of a typical building project consists of materials. The profit of many building companies is limited to $2\frac{1}{2}\%$ of turnover. In such circumstances a small percentage saving of 1% on material costs will increase net profit by 20%.

In this chapter the function of the builders' merchant, buying procedures and the wastage of materials are examined in detail.

THE BUILDERS' MERCHANT

The majority of materials and components used in the building industry are distributed through builders' merchants, who act as intermediaries between the manufacturer and the builder.

Traditionally there was a tendency for merchants to specialise in a particular range of products.

(a) Heavy merchants who supplied such materials as bricks, blocks, roof tiles, drainage goods, cement, concrete products, sand, aggregate, plaster, plasterboard.
(b) Light merchants who supplied, for example, sanitary ware, ironmongery, plumbers' fittings, kitchen fittings, wall and floor tiles, paint.
(c) Timber merchants who supplied sawn and wrought timber, building boards and standard joinery.

(d) Specialist merchants who supplied a single range of products, such as glass, plumbing materials or electrical fittings.

These divisions were never clear, but today they have become even more blurred. The majority of merchants have expanded their traditional range of products to include many of the lines of other specialist merchants, although their origins can usually be identified by their expertise and competitive quotations in the original, narrower range of materials. The impetus for this change, and the development of multi-branch expansion has been generated in part by the growth of the do-it-yourself market.

A parallel trend has developed of increased specialisation in a narrow range of products, such as windows and doors, decorating materials, or floor and wall tiling, but with a dual market of trade and retail for do-it-yourself. These companies tend to seek high street or easily accessible trading locations in order to achieve a competitive thrust, and often operate on a cash and carry basis for both trade and retail. Building materials are also being marketed by hypermarkets at very competitive prices, not only to DIY enthusiasts, but also to the jobbing builder and small builder.

Some larger builders may buy directly from the manufacturer rather than via the merchant, but overall such arrangements will only represent a small proportion of materials purchased.

FUNCTION OF THE MERCHANT
The builders' merchant provides a number of invaluable services to the builder. The most signficant of these are the provision of credit, the availability of stock, an efficient delivery service and technical advice on the use of materials.

Credit facilities
Most builders' merchants offer the builder credit facilities in the form of a monthly account, whereby goods supplied in one calendar month are required to be paid for by the last day of the following month. In the 1960s and early 1970s, longer periods of credit were negotiated by builders, often up to four months; high interest charges, market instability and bankruptcy have curtailed such facilities. Nevertheless, even today, many companies have retained six-weekly accounts with some merchants.

The majority of builders' merchants offer a $2\frac{1}{2}\%$ cash discount provided payment is received within the agreed credit period. Some merchants offer high cash discounts of $3\frac{3}{4}\%$ or 5%, but usually in exchange for early settlement of their account. Where no discount is allowed, the builder has less incentive to pay his account promptly and may as a consequence delay payment, and thus extend his credit by an additional two or three weeks without 'aggravating' the merchant. Some suppliers, to counteract such behaviour by the builder, either 'stop' the account or add a credit surcharge to the invoice.

The actual credit available, therefore, is a give and take situation where individual contractors and merchants reach a compromise. Even where cash discount is allowed for prompt settlement the merchant may allow up to 10 days of grace for late payment without loss of discount. This extension to credit facilities, probably on average three days, can make a significant contribution to the builder's cash flow, particularly when large sums of money are involved.

Occasionally, the builder may be obliged to obtain materials from a supplier where credit facilities have not been arranged, or direct from a manufacturer. In such circumstances a pro-forma invoice may be raised by the supplier, and the builder requested to pay all, or a substantial proportion, of the total cost before the goods will be delivered.

Credit control

The builders' merchant with local knowledge and contacts can carefully monitor the track record of construction companies and expand or contract credit accordingly. Credit control of this nature would be virtually impossible if many thousands of individual builders traded directly with the manufacturer. The intermediary role of the builders' merchant is therefore beneficial to both the builder and manufacturer.

Stock

The merchant holds stocks of materials and components in order to meet the builder's immediate requirements. This buffer stock is of considerable advantage to the builder in avoiding delivery delays from the manufacturer. In practice many merchants maintain stock at minimum levels to avoid high overhead costs, but the efficient contractor with a well organised buying department will in any event be ordering materials sufficiently far in advance to allow for the manufacturers' delivery periods.

When materials are in short supply, the individual merchants will receive a weekly or monthly allocation from the manufacturer. In such circumstances the merchant is likely to re-allocate to the customer who regularly trades with him and who settles the account promptly.

Ex-works deliveries

Many materials, particularly in the heavy classification, are supplied direct by the manufacturer to the builder's yard or site. In such cases the merchant is merely providing a management service. The mark-up on the ex-works price of the manufacturer will be approximately 5% plus transport costs. Some merchants, particularly in depressed market conditions, will even offer the builder a reduction of 1% to 2% on this commission.

In certain circumstances the merchant may combine orders for part loads for different builders or sites, thus alleviating a part load surcharge. Where materials normally supplied ex-works are purchased from stocks held at the merchant's yard, either because of the small quantities involved or due to urgent delivery requirements, then merchants will impose a surcharge of 20% plus for storage, double-handling and delivery.

Trade discount

The percentage profit the merchant expects on cost will vary between 5% for materials delivered direct by the manufacturer to site and up to at least 50% on some other products. How much of this margin the merchant is prepared to pass on to the builder either in reduced prices or trade discount is determined by market conditions, size of order, customer loyalty, skill of buyer, status of builder, site location, availability and level of stock. Many merchants operate on the basis of a standard trade discount of 10%, while others, particularly those specialising in a single range of products, operate a sliding discount structure of up to, say 40% off retail.

Some merchants also operate a system where loyalty or cumulative rebates are offered, provided purchases exceed levels predetermined between the supplier and the buyer. National companies may also agree bulk purchase rates with individual merchants or manufacturers.

Service

The service received by the builder will vary widely between one merchant and another. Some merchants offer next day delivery, six days a week, exyard stock, while others may plan delivery on an area basis and only provide a weekly or twice-weekly service. The delivery period of timber and other specialised merchants may well vary between one day and three weeks, depending on market pressures and the time taken to process materials, such as the planing of timber.

Inefficiency of the builder's management structure, lack of forward planning, or emergency requirements, will result in some builders placing more emphasis on service than on cost. Those merchants offering next day delivery may wish to achieve a higher profit margin to offset the probable disruption in route planning and area deliveries. As mentioned earlier, some merchants operate on a cash and carry basis but offer very competitive prices in lieu of delivery service.

Technical representatives

The builders' merchant's representatives can be of invaluable assistance to the contractor. On their regular visits to the builder's office they provide advice on delivery periods, shortages, price increases, new materials, tenders and tender results. The representatives also deal with invoice queries, shortages and breakages upon delivery, and will provide trade literature or obtain technical information on request. Many manufacturers employ their own independent representatives who are sometimes highly qualified and provide technical information and advice on fixing and use of their company's products, while others only function as salesmen. The buyer will need to use discretion concerning how much time is allocated to representatives and will probably see the majority of them only by appointment.

BUYING DEPARTMENT

The majority of builders form a buying department to undertake the purchase of materials. The department will provide four basic functions – taking off and scheduling quantities, purchasing, progressing outstanding orders, and clerical work including checking invoices. In smaller companies all these functions will be undertaken by one or two persons, but in larger companies a degree of specialisation is probable. It is essential that the buyer is a person of integrity, tact and tenacity and has effective negotiating ability together with the necessary expertise to select the right supplier.

BUYING OBJECTIVES
The primary objectives of the buying department are to:

(a) Purchase materials at the most competitive cost.
(b) Ensure that the correct quantities of materials are ordered and delivered.
(c) Ascertain that the quality of supplies is in accordance with the bill of quantities, specification and contract drawings.
(d) Obtain all materials at the correct time in accordance with the project programme.
(e) Minimise waste and provide site management with cutting and stacking schedules.
(f) Check and approve invoices for payment.
(g) Feed back materials cost information to the estimating department and management.

BUYING PROCEDURES
The buying process involves a number of separate operations and for clarity these will be discussed in the approximate order of occurrence.

Enquiry
The first stage in the buying procedure is the enquiry from the builder to the supplier for a quotation for the required materials. Some enquiries will have been sent out at tender stage, while the estimate was being prepared. The subsequent quotations are passed from the estimating to the buying department for information or utilisation as required. Enquiries should be sent out for all materials needed for a project as soon as possible in order to highlight any transport or supply problems.

The enquiry should be as comprehensive as possible to avoid queries and delays at a later date, and should preferably be in a printed format with the name and address of the builder, and clearly marked 'enquiry'. Sufficient information should be provided to clearly identify the product, such as detailed specification, bill of quantity extract, British Standard reference, manufacturers' or catalogue reference number, together with the approximate quantity required, the delivery date and the location of the site.

The buyer will be aware from previous experience of the most competitive and reliable sources of materials. Normally enquiries will be sent to at least three such suppliers, unless there is a single source of supply. The exact number of enquiries for each commodity will be left to the discretion of the buyer.

Enquiries are preferably made in writing, but under the pressure of circumstances the buyer may undertake enquiries by telephone.

Quotation

The supplier, who may be a builders' merchant or manufacturer, will in response to a written or verbal enquiry prepare a quotation.

The buying department will examine and compare quotations to establish:

(a) The most competitive price subject to comparable quality.
(b) Quality of the product.
(c) Different delivery conditions, for example ex-works, additional carriage charges, mechanical off-load charges, pallet or packing charges, restricted turn-round time for supplier's transport which, when extended, results in penalty charges.
(d) The discount structure offered by each supplier, including cash discounts, trade discounts, loyalty and cumulative rebates.
(e) The delivery period and, in the case of call off orders, the ability to maintain supply and any associated conditions.
(f) Whether the price includes or excludes VAT.
(g) Whether any items are subject to a percentage surcharge, for example preservation treatment of timber.
(h) Whether the price quoted is fixed or subject to increase after a defined period. Quotations may also be subject to price ruling at date of despatch, particularly when the price stability is affected by external factors, such as the value of the pound for imported materials.

The above check-list is not exhaustive and great care and skill is necessary in comparing quotations to establish the best buy.

When a final comparison is made of quotations received, marginal increases in prices above expectation may be revealed. This might indicate that the majority or all the suppliers of a commodity in a geographical area have formed a ring or cartel. Such practices are illegal under the Fair Trading Act of 1973. The suppliers who have formed the ring meet on a regular basis to agree prices, to decide how orders are to be shared, and which supplier will quote the lowest price. Rings can be broken, either by obtaining additional quotations, if necessary from outside the immediate geographical area, or by reporting the suppliers to the Director of Fair Trading.

Calculation of quantities

Usually there will be a disclaimer in the preliminaries advising the builder that the client's quantity surveyor will not accept responsibility for any loss or expense arising from the use of the bill of quantities for ordering. Notwithstanding, the buyer may choose to use the bill to extract the quantity of material required. Experience, however, will reveal that the bill is often unreliable and that if errors lead to incorrect purchasing, it is unlikely that any claim made against the client or his quantity surveyor for any loss or expense incurred could be substantiated. The correct practice, therefore, will be for the buying department to take off or prepare schedules of quantities from the latest revision of the contract drawings. The taking off should be annotated and kept in work sections or elements in order that all materials can be clearly identified and given a site location reference. It may prove beneficial to use check-lists to ensure that no individual items are overlooked.

One accurate remeasurement will reduce waste and eliminate continual remeasurement of the project, and can be utilised for:

- purchasing of materials
- preparation of cutting and stacking schedules for site foreman
- base quantities for payment of sub-contract labour or direct labour on a bonus scheme
- identification of discrepancies between the latest revision of the contract drawings, specification and bill of quantities and the subsequent raising of a variation order for inclusion in the final account

Timing of deliveries

The delivery of materials must be synchronised with the contract programme as supplies delivered out of sequence with site operations can either cause storage difficulties or alternatively delays and disruptions. The buyer needs to be alert to amendments to the contract programme and should keep in close contact with both the site and the contract manager, either verbally or in writing. Daily or weekly site reports are a useful management tool to achieve this purpose. A typical example is shown in Figure 5.1.

The buyer must also be aware of problems which may affect the timing of deliveries, such as changing market conditions and subsequent shortages and surpluses, stock levels, strikes, holidays, close-downs and transport difficulties. Delivery periods can rapidly be extended with only a slight upturn in the market, particularly where the builders' merchants

Weekly Development Site Report

| Project | | | | Job No. | | Date | |

Progress					Date Occupied	Brief Weather Details
Plot No.	Stage Reached		Anticipated Completion Date	Anticipated Delays		
						Mon
						Tues
						Wed
						Thurs
						Fri
						Sat
						Visitors to Site
						Mon
						Tues
						Wed
						Thurs
						Fri
						Sat
Road						
Storm Sewer						
Foul Sewer						
Main Services						
Gas						
Water						
Electric						

Labour on Site	Mon	Tues	Wed	Thurs	Fri	Sat	Plant Required	Date Required	Reason
Bricklayers									
Carpenters									
Plasterers									
Plumbers							Plant Supplied	Date for Removal	
Painters									
Labourers									
Ground Workers									
Tilers - Roof							Details of Plant Repairs Required		
- Floor									
- Wall									
Totals									

Material Receipts (Please attach Delivery Notes)				Details of Delays / Decisions Required
Delivery Note No.	Quantity	Description	Supplier	Material and Labour Requirements

Shortages/Damages to be reported in 'Description' Column

Signed_____

Fig. 5.1 Weekly site report

or manufacturers maintain only a low level of stock and the manufacturers' productive capacity is inelastic. The buyer should be aware of such factors from regular contact with the builders' merchant's representative, study of trade journals and the national press.

Official order

Orders should be in writing and on the company's official order form, clearly setting out the company's name and address. Each order should be consecutively numbered to avoid the possibility of fraud and to permit easy identification.

The purchase order is usually an offer by the builder to purchase materials and becomes a legal contract when the supplier accepts or executes the order. Many companies include conditions on the reverse side of the company's standard order form, which may conflict with, and possibly override, the conditions on the reverse side of the supplier's quotation.

The order format when completed should be clear, concise and include the following basic information:

- date of order
- contract number
- specification of goods required, including sizes or weights, the quantity required and the price
- quotation reference, date and the date delivery is required
- the site or delivery address and directions where necessary
- bill of quantities or site location reference to assist the site foreman and contract manager
- signature of authorised personnel

It may be advisable to define the times and dates deliveries will be accepted on site. Special arrangements for packaging and unloading, such as pallets or crane off-load, should be made where necessary. If access to the site is restricted the supplier should be advised of the type, size and weight of transport that can be accepted.

Where companies utilise printed order forms a common method is to bind orders into pads, with four copies of each order, usually in different colours for easy identification:

- White – original   to supplier
- Yellow – first copy   to site/contract manager/stores
- Green – second copy   retained by buying department
- Pink – third copy   to accounts department

Site orders

In order to maintain financial control of building activities many companies restrict the purchasing of materials to the buying department. In certain circumstances, however, for such bulk items as cement, sand, and aggregate, the buyer may place a blanket order with a supplier and the site foreman or contract manager will call off deliveries as required. The site foreman may also have a special order form with an imposed cash limit per order of, say, £50 for emergency purchases only.

In many smaller companies the buying function will be carried out completely by the site foreman. This obviously has many disadvantages. On very large contracts on the other hand, buying may be undertaken by specialist staff from a site office with the advantage of direct contact with contract management and planning personnel.

Advice note

The supplier or manufacturer may acknowledge receipt of the order by means of an advice note, giving a description of the goods and either the date materials were dispatched and method of transport, or the expected date of arrival on site. The advice note may also provide details of any special equipment or assistance required for unloading.

Delivery note

When goods are delivered to the site or the builder's yard, the supplier will provide two copies of the delivery note detailing the quantity and specification of goods supplied. One copy of the delivery ticket will be required to be signed by the site foreman or other authorised representative and returned with the driver to the supplier, confirming that the goods have been delivered. The merchant will normally only accept complaints regarding shortages or breakages if acknowledged at the time, either by an appropriate note on the delivery ticket or in writing within a maximum of three days.

The foreman or other authorised representative is, therefore, responsible for checking the quantity, quality and condition of goods received. This task can be both difficult and onerous, particularly when materials are packed in crates or delivered in large quantities, such as tiles on pallets. Where it is impossible to check materials delivered, the delivery ticket should be clearly signed as unexamined; furthermore, if goods are returned to the supplier this fact should be clearly entered on the ticket.

Failure to check delivery tickets adequately may well encourage the unscrupulous driver to short-deliver on future occasions.

The second copy of the delivery ticket, together with any comments made on the top copy, will be returned on a daily or weekly basis to the head office, buying department or accounts department, together with a materials return sheet. This is a format in duplicate listing all materials delivered to the site each day. An alternative procedure is to incorporate a materials delivered section in the daily or weekly site report.

The site copy of the materials return sheet can be utilised by the foreman as a record of the date and quantity of goods delivered and the identification of outstanding orders. If materials are supplied without a delivery ticket the foreman should make a ticket in order to maintain the company's records. Loss of delivery tickets can seriously hamper the routine checking of invoices.

Where materials are transferred from one site to another or returned to the company's yard, materials transfer forms should be used. Both incoming and outgoing materials should be clearly recorded on the materials return sheet or site report. Where a company printed format is not available, the foreman should make materials transfer forms using a standard duplicate book.

One small point that should be mentioned is that frequently when goods have been loaded by fork-lift and off-loaded by crane, any pallets used are charged out at a high rate. The foreman should, therefore, set such pallets aside, clearly identified for each supplier, for return with the next delivery, and mark the paperwork accordingly. If no further deliveries are expected a memorandum should be sent to the suppliers, requesting the uplift of pallets and the issue of the necessary credit note.

Invoice

The invoice is the uniquely numbered document raised by the supplier listing the goods supplied to the builder together with the prices and dispatch date or delivery date. It will also provide details of any trade discount, cash discount and VAT.

The supplier as part of his administrative procedure will often produce the advice note, delivery note and invoice at the same time with identical information, except that the invoice alone will be priced, at a later date. Two copies of the invoice are usually required by the builder, one copy for the financial accounts and one copy for the cost accounts. The explanation for this requirement is given in Chapter 9.

Authorisation of payment

Before payment is made the invoice should be checked against the quotation, order and delivery note to identify any error in price, quantity, quality, delivery delays or damage. The importance of invoice checking is frequently overlooked by company management and the responsibility delegated to junior or inexperienced staff. Even when this is not the case, boredom, frustration or lack of time can lead to invoices being passed for payment with errors that have been overlooked. A comprehensive and thorough quotation, order and invoice checking procedure can result in substantial savings and thus increased profit potential.

Generally where a builder fails to obtain quotations, the supplier will tend to marginally increase prices. Moreover, some suppliers quote competitive prices, but invoice at marginally higher rates, on the assumption that a substantial percentage of contractors will fail to identify such adjustments when or if invoices are checked. Frequently, if a builder deals exclusively with the same supplier for a range of commodities, prices may not be competitive and where the builder, as a result of bad management, invariably requires urgent or next day delivery, the supplier will tend to charge higher prices.

Statement

The supplier will send a statement to the builder each month of the invoices rendered during that calendar month. The statement will set out details of each invoice, including the invoice number, the invoice amount, VAT, discount and the corresponding total values. No distinction will be made on the statement between invoices for different projects.

The statement will usually be retained by the company accountant in order to reconcile the relevant bought ledger account and monitor the checking of the respective invoices, and will form the basis of payment.

Progressing outstanding orders

The general foreman or site agent will receive on site one copy of all orders placed by the buyer. In view of the fact that contract progress is dependent on delivery of materials at the correct time the foreman will have the direct responsibility for ensuring that outstanding orders are expedited by the supplier. It will be prudent for the foreman to telephone suppliers several days prior to scheduled delivery dates to confirm that no problems are envisaged and that promised delivery dates will be adhered to.

The most common method of monitoring deliveries is to file all outstanding orders in anticipated delivery date order and expedite them immediately they are overdue. Occasionally cancellation and re-ordering will be necessary.

FILING PROCEDURES

The buying process generates large volumes of paper and an efficient and accurate filing system is essential for monitoring and management control. At least a basic filing system should be maintained for each contract as follows:

(a) enquiry file – containing copies of all enquiries, unacceptable quotations received and any schedules prepared to compare quotations.

(b) Quotation file – containing all quotations that have been or are due to be accepted.

(c) Order and delivery note file – containing all outstanding orders and corresponding delivery tickets, where invoices have not been checked. Orders can be filed alphabetically under the name of the merchant and in date sequence.

(d) 'Invoiced' order and delivery note file – as invoices are checked both the copy order and delivery note should be cancelled (stamped *PASSED*), removed from the order and delivery note file and re-filed. This invoiced order and delivery note file will save time lost in working through dead paperwork.

(e) Invoice file – containing invoices received by the buying department and due to be checked and returned to the accounts department.

For large projects the files could be sub-divided alphabetically either for different suppliers or separate trades.

CO-ORDINATED AND BULK BUYING

Certain advantages can be obtained by the builder if buying for various contracts is co-ordinated or undertaken in bulk. The buyer in such cases will negotiate prices with the merchant on a term basis, often nationwide, subject to all orders for that material being placed with the supplier. Alternatively the supplier may offer rebates if predetermined levels of purchases are achieved. It is important to appreciate that the purchasing power of many builders is dissipated by buying from numerous sources and in small quantities.

Some national companies have expanded vertically by taking over builders' merchants, manufacturers or suppliers of sand, gravel, etc., thus securing for themselves preferential treatment in both supply and price.

INDUSTRIALISATION

The buyer, in consultation with the contracts manager or surveyor, may be involved in management decisions regarding the level of prefabrication or off-site assembly – for example, the choice between the use of roof trusses or traditional construction. Each situation will need to be judged on its own merits to take account of handling, waste, cost, reduction in site labour requirements and cash flow.

STORES – STOCK AND STOCK CONTROL

Many companies, particularly those involved with small works, maintain their own stores department. Some savings can be expected where purchases such as cement can be made in bulk and redistributed in small quantities. A small works department, moreover, will need easy access to supplies to maintain efficiency. Normally, however, maintaining own stores is less efficient and more costly than either cross-counter purchases or direct delivery by a merchant to site, due to:

- cost of double-handling of materials
- overhead costs (rent, rates, heating, lighting) in maintaining storage space
- interest on capital locked up in stores, racking, bins, etc.
- additional staff costs to manage the store
- deterioration of and damage to materials

One advantage in maintaining a store is that materials may be recycled when returned from site, upon completion of a contract.

DOCUMENTATION

Internal documentation will be needed to support a stores department as follows:

(a) Stores requisition – in place of the official order.
(b) Stores issue note – in lieu of the delivery note. The stores issue note should be in triplicate with one copy to site, one copy retained by stores department and one copy to accounts department.

(c) The accounts copy of the stores issue note will be priced and substituted for the invoice.

(d) Materials transfer note – materials transferred between sites or returned from the site to the store should be recorded on a materials transfer note in order that the costing of individual projects can be adjusted.

STOCK CONTROL

Building materials are frequently bulky and consequently occupy substantial floor area when taken into the store. For the efficient management of stores, therefore, it is essential to maintain a stock control policy.

On completion of a contract where surplus materials are due to be returned from the site to the store, careful consideration should be given to establish whether:

(a) the materials could be returned to the supplier and a credit obtained
(b) the materials should be scrapped
(c) the materials could be re-used on other projects within a reasonable period of time and should, therefore, be taken into the store
(d) the materials could be moved direct to another site for use in that project

Failure to adhere to a decisive policy regarding surplus materials will result in the all-too familiar jumble observed in many builders' yards.

Stock levels should be monitored and the movement of each stock item checked over a weekly, monthly or three-monthly period. Large quantities of stock with very slow movement should be avoided, disposed of or written down in value, depending on circumstances. Materials with limited shelf life or subject to damage or deterioration should only be stocked if they are in constant demand.

The materials store and yard should be adequately protected against theft and vandalism.

GIFTS AND INDUCEMENTS

The buyer may be induced to place orders with a supplier by the acceptance of free lunches or gifts. Obviously the buyer should exercise great care to avoid being placed under any obligation in this way, which may well be to the detriment not only of the company, but also of the buyer's reputation.

A traditional Christmas or annual lunch with a main supplier, or the acceptance of a *small* Christmas gift, may be acceptable, provided such transactions are with the knowledge and approval of the directors of both the supplier and the builder.

WASTE

Unfortunately waste is a serious problem in the construction industry and therefore any discussion on materials purchasing cannot be concluded without an analysis of this problem.

Waste occurs at each and every stage of the construction process: design, ordering, transport and delivery, site storage, fixing and placing in position, and through vandalism and theft prior to handover. *BRE Digest 247* also identifies indirect waste where materials are used either for purposes other than those specified or in excess of the measured quantities.

DESIGN WASTE

Waste at the design stage is outside the parameters of this book, but the following are the key causes:

(a) The dimensions of materials may be ignored, with the consequence that waste will occur in cutting to size.
(b) Failure to use standard production items or standard size components.
(c) Lack of design information, delayed instructions and excessive or delayed variations to the contract. In each case the contractor may well make wrong assumptions when placing orders with the consequential risk of over-ordering.
(d) Lack of dimensional co-ordination.

ORDERING WASTE

The buyer traditionally allows a percentage addition to the calculated quantities of most materials for waste, for example 5% addition for bricks and blocks. Such additions vary with individual materials and from company to company. These percentage additions may bear little resemblance to the actual waste on site and may even be in excess of the amounts required. Figure 5.2, extracted from *BRE Digest 247*, sets out the results of a study of percentage wastage over eight different materials on

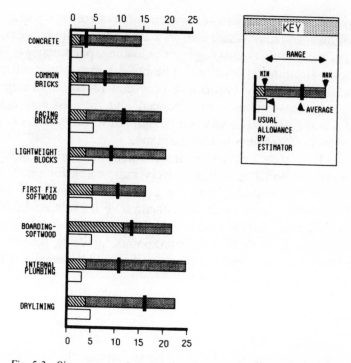

Fig. 5.2 Site wastage of materials (drawn from BRE Digest 247)

230 sites. Some items such as doors, windows, and sanitary ware, will obviously be ordered net. Careful and accurate scheduling and taking off will obviously result in less waste than ordering direct from the bill of quantities or merely estimating quantities.

The buyer may also contribute directly to improved control of waste by ordering, for example, packaged ironmongery with the exact number of screws required rather than separate locks, latches, door furniture and boxes of screws.

TRANSPORT AND DELIVERY WASTE

The majority of materials are subject to possible damage during loading, transit or off-loading. Modern methods of packaging and delivery include pallets, loading by fork-lift and unloading by crane. This has reduced breakages, but such savings have been partly offset, from the builder's viewpoint, by the exact quantity delivered being invoiced; in the past it was customary for manufacturers to add a small surplus quantity to the materials delivered to site, to offset any breakages, for example bricks, blocks and tiles.

Damage is more likely to occur where drivers are on a bonus scheme for fast turn-round, or where deliveries are undertaken by hire companies. This is primarily due to negligent unloading, particularly of joinery, sanitary ware, plasterboard, etc. The builder may also contribute to unloading damage by insufficient provision of labour, resulting for example in heavy items being dropped and their corners damaged. Deliveries are often made well outside normal working hours and items are 'thrown off' through lack of assistance.

It has been stated earlier in this chapter that the site foreman or authorised personnel accepting delivery must check for shortages and breakages, thus ensuring that the cost of any loss is, if possible, transferred to the supplier or manufacturer. For example, brick packs should be examined at the time of delivery for damage at corners and for broken bricks above the fork-lift insert points. Similarly, items subject to deterioration (cement, plasterboard, etc.) should be examined for any water penetration during transit.

SITE STORAGE WASTE

Probably more waste occurs from poor site storage than from any other circumstance. The decision as to where to store materials on site is a key factor in both the wastage of materials and the additional labour incurred in double-handling. Snap decisions on where to place materials by the site foreman or the labour on site usually lead to a need to relocate before fixing. The buyer should be requested to provide stacking schedules detailing (for example) the quantity and types of plasterboard to be used in different parts of the building.

Before work commences on site the general foreman, contract manager and planner should liaise to analyse in detail the most suitable areas for storage of all material deliveries, as follows:

(a) Define the area of building operations including an allowance for scaffolding and access, together with ancillary work, such as drainage, service roads, paths and paving.
(b) Decide on the location of site huts, dry store for storage of cement etc. to avoid water damage, and a secure compound for open storage of materials subject to theft or vandalism.
(c) Plan the location of temporary roads and hardstanding for all other materials in order to ensure that lorries can reach storage areas safely and easily. This can be particularly important as many suppliers will

not permit their vehicles onto the site unless there is a well consolidated temporary road.

(d) Plan routes for movement of materials and plant around the site with ample allowance for width of dumpers and other plant and vehicles, to avoid damage to stocks of materials.

(e) By reference to the contract programme and working drawings, define stage and timing at which areas of both the site and the building may be used to store materials without hindrance to later operations.

(f) Material storage points should be as close as possible to point of use to reduce double-handling and consequent damage.

(g) Consideration should also be given to storage conditions, for example hardstanding for bricks, blocks and drainage goods, racks and waterproof covering for timber, timber retaining for aggregate and sand to avoid loss through spreading, and level storage for windows and door frames to avoid twisting.

CUTTING WASTE

Some waste from cutting is inevitable, but the use of skilled and conscientious labour will keep this waste to a minimum: for example, the bricklayer who uses broken bricks as bats instead of cutting them, or the plasterer who sets out plasterboard during fixing to utilise offcuts. Conversely, unskilled or uncaring labour can dramatically increase cutting waste.

Cutting waste on timber can be substantial as timber is only supplied in incremental lengths of 300 mm. The site foreman or buyer should be particularly aware of the practice of some timber merchants of sending out the nearest length above, if the length ordered is not in stock, i.e. 5.1 metres in lieu of 4.8 metres. This will result in substantial additional waste and to counteract this practice orders should be placed with the provision that only the ordered length will be paid for.

HANDLING AND FIXING WASTE

Lack of care, concern or skill on the part of the operative can result in extensive loss of and damage to materials. For example:

(a) Materials dropped or discarded – bricks or half bricks, nails, screws, wall ties, scaffold fittings – paint tins left open, etc.

(b) Overmixing of mortar by bricklayers' labourers, resulting in surplus at the end of the working day. Similarly, over-production of concrete or over-ordering, if pre-mixed.

(c) Failure to cut timber in accordance with the buyer's cutting schedule.
(d) Poor setting out and cutting of sheet materials.
(e) Damage to stocks of materials and the structure during movement on site of material and plant.

VANDALISM

Vandalism can be a major problem to builders, particularly in inner-city sites, where it is probable that the majority of damage is caused by children under 14. A secure site perimeter fence at least 2 metres high, with locking entrance gates, is a useful deterrent. In addition, a securely fenced materials compound is essential.

In areas of high risk it may be economic to employ a professional security company, either on the basis of permanent manning outside working hours or, as more commonly practised, periodic visits to the site.

THEFT

Petty theft, either by site operatives or the local inhabitants, particularly on housing developments, can reach significant proportions. Management can restrict such activities by maintaining accurate stock control and tight security measures and also ensuring that operatives' cars are parked well away from materials stocks. In addition, spot checks can be carried out at evenings and weekends and floodlighting used to deter the professional thief.

INDIRECT WASTE

Substitution

Indirect waste arises where materials are used for a different purpose than that specified. For example, facing bricks used in place of common bricks, concrete used of higher strength than specified. Substitution of this nature will result in a monetary rather than material loss.

On-site production waste

Production methods may result in wastage, for example failure to achieve an economic utilisation of formwork.

Negligent waste
Inefficient or incompetent site management may generate negligent waste. For example, excessive excavation of trenches or oversite excavation, resulting in additional use of concrete or hardcore.

6 Directly Employed Labour and Sub-contractors

INTRODUCTION

Traditionally, labour in the construction industry has been employed on a casual basis. The location of a builder's work is continuously changing, and labour is frequently engaged at the commencement of a project and laid off upon completion.

In the construction industry, as in other industries, mechanisation and industrialised systems have had, and continue to have, an important impact in reducing demand for labour. Work on site, however, even in the 1980s remains fairly labour-intensive. As well as changes in technique, market conditions at any particular time will, of course, affect the demand for labour. The economic recession of the '70s and '80s has inevitably led to a fall in the recruitment and training of skilled operatives, coupled with a loss of skilled tradesmen to other, less depressed industries.

The nature of the building industry does, however, generate a resourceful, independent and adaptable labour force, with an entrepreneurial spirit. This in turn has led to systems of employment of labour which, while not unique, yet display a measure of variety and flexibility rarely encountered in other industries. Although many builders continue to use directly employed labour, a pronounced tendency has developed to employ labour on a sub-contract basis, particularly in southern England.

The term sub-contractor may apply equally to a private or public company, any corporate or public body, as well as any individual self-employed person or partnership.

In this chapter, directly employed labour and the three classes of sub-contractor – labour-only, labour and material, and nominated – are examined, together with the problems of training, and feedback of labour costs to management.

LABOUR-ONLY SUB-CONTRACTORS

Labour-only sub-contractors supply their labour and, in addition, may provide small tools and plant, but they will not be responsible for the provision of materials. Labour-only sub-contractors may generally be viewed as a substitute for directly employed labour.

Concern has been expressed periodically by architects, trade unions, the Construction Industry Training Board and both central and local government, at the growth in use of labour-only sub-contractors. This concern has been mainly concentrated on quality of work, training, avoidance of payment of income tax or national insurance, and conditions of employment. It could be argued that to a large extent such fears are unfounded or else that the difficulties have been overcome.

The growth of labour-only sub-contracting has been of mutual benefit to both employers and employees. It should be emphasised, however, that one major reason for the growth in its use has been the effect in recent years of the additional legislation bearing upon employment and the increased cost and risks of employing operatives direct.

In this chapter, when examining the benefits and disadvantages of labour-only sub-contracting to both the builder and sub-contractor, it will be apparent that the builder probably receives the greater benefit.

Where a labour-only sub-contractor employs the work-force direct, operates the PAYE scheme and pays a set wage, the employee of the sub-contractor is in a similar position to the employee of the builder. The builder, however, will view such operatives as sub-contractors.

BENEFITS TO THE SUB-CONTRACTOR

The main incentive for building trade workers to go on their own and become labour-only sub-contractors is the opportunity to increase their earnings. This increase comes from improved productivity, longer working hours, higher rates, or from a percentage of the earnings of labourers and craftsmen that they themselves employ. In addition there will be tax advantages where it may prove possible, for example, for the sub-contractor to offset against income tax telephone charges, rates, heating and lighting, car or van expenses and the payment, say, to a member of the family for the preparation of accounts.

Many operatives also welcome the independence and freedom, within the limits set by the builder, to choose working hours and in certain circumstances to work unlimited overtime. There is an added freedom to choose the location of work, although the cost of any travelling involved will usually be the responsibility of the sub-contractor.

Many labour-only sub-contractors have grasped the opportunity to expand initially to a labour and material sub-contractor and subsequently to a general contractor.

DISADVANTAGES TO THE SUB-CONTRACTOR

The disadvantages faced by the labour-only sub-contractor are numerous compared to those of the directly employed operative. Not least are the risks transferred from the builder to the sub-contractor (discussed in detail later in this chapter under 'benefits to the builder'). The sub-contractor will also have an increased administrative burden in providing annual accounts for the Inland Revenue, preparing estimates and calculating and monitoring payments to employees irrespective of whether they are self-employed or engaged on the PAYE scheme. It should be borne in mind that many labour-only sub-contractors lack administrative and management ability and therefore find themselves in financial difficulties when employing labour or expanding their gang size.

The sub-contractor is dependent on the builder for regular payment for the work carried out. Occasionally the builder may raise minor maintenance problems to justify his failure to pay for work executed or to release retention. The sub-contractor then has to make the difficult choice of continuing work in the hope of being paid, or withdrawing his labour and reducing the probability of ultimate payment. Moreover, particularly with smaller firms, the builder may be unable to pay owing to cash flow problems, receivership or bankruptcy.

Self-employed persons generally receive less help from the state in periods of unemployment or sickness. Under the social security system no unemployment benefit is paid and entitlement to supplementary benefit will only arise when savings are below a predetermined level. The DHSS provide sick pay contributions to the self-employed, but at a lower level than that paid to an employed operative. State retirement pensions are also at a lower level.

BENEFITS TO THE BUILDER

Generally, builders stand to gain in a number of ways from encouraging self-employment in the construction industry. As these factors are examined it is important to bear in mind that a major advantage to the builder is that the financial risks of employing labour direct are transferred to the sub-contractor.

Production costs

When employing labour direct the builder is committed to pay his employees, irrespective of the quantity and quality of their output. The labour-only sub-contractor, however, although occasionally employed on an hourly rate, will invariably be allocated work on a unit rate or lump sum basis and will only be paid for the actual work produced. This will result in effective cost control for the builder. Responsibility for loss of earnings and production, due to inclement weather for example, will rest with the sub-contractor.

Overheads and administration

Administration and overhead costs to the builder will be reduced for such items as national insurance contributions, holidays with pay, sick pay, tool money and redundancy payments. Theoretically the sub-contractor should make provision for these on-costs in the rates or daywork rate agreed with the builder, but frequently the provision is inadequate.

Continuity

Lack of continuity of work for labour can occur on an individual project, between one project and the next, or as a result of changes in the location of construction activity. It is the responsibility of the sub-contractor to overcome such problems by finding alternative employment during these periods, or by bearing the cost of the unemployment.

Transport costs

The sub-contractor will be responsible for transporting his work-force to the site and for any travelling time or expenses. In general, therefore, sub-contract labour will tend to be more mobile than directly employed labour. However, the builder may be expected to make some contribution towards travelling time and costs where he has failed to obtain suitable sub-contract labour within the vicinity of the site and a sub-contractor is requested to travel an excessive distance.

Quality control

It is a commonly stated opinion that the quality of work produced by sub-contractors is below the standard of that achieved by directly employed labour, particularly where pride in workmanship is overshadowed by a potential increase in earnings. However, to a large extent the converse is true because:

(a) There is a tendency for the more skilled tradesmen to prefer to work as sub-contractors.
(b) Not only does the builder hold a retention of from 5% to 10%, but also up to a week's payment in hand, and the release of either will be subject to the sub-contractor achieving a satisfactory quality of work. The builder, therefore, has the ultimate control in that no payment need be made for sub-standard work.
(c) The sense of responsibility held by most sub-contractors is such that they will be concerned to retain their reputation as tradesmen, particularly bearing in mind the need for continuity of employment.

Reduced supervision
The sub-contractor is motivated by the need to maximise his earnings. Therefore, he will take positive steps to establish the nature of the task, the material and plant requirements, including their availability and proximity to the work place, and the contract programme and its impact on flow of work and future workload. Moreover, the sub-contractor will probably develop the ability to work on his own initiative and will ensure that management is positive, forward-thinking and alert. (Any weakness in management is, therefore, more likely to be exposed by the use of sub-contract labour.)

Market conditions
Competition between sub-contractors may lead to lower rates, particularly when the market is depressed. The opposite will also apply of course, and labour-only sub-contract rates are sometimes more related to market conditions than to the actual work content. In times of boom, any high rates which by necessity are being paid on one site, may by discussion with other sub-contractors in that trade result in a demand for similar increases on other sites.

DISADVANTAGES TO THE BUILDER
The reliability of some sub-contractors may be questionable. If they are able to 'overdraw' on their payments, or to obtain improved rates on

other sites, they may withdraw their labour without notice. The builder can of course withhold any payment or retention outstanding, but this will probably not offset the cost of delay and disturbance in locating an alternative sub-contractor. Equally, programming of work may be more complicated, particularly where sub-contract labour fails to conform to the contract programme, or labour is withdrawn.

Sub-contract labour may be hard to obtain for certain types of work: for example, small works where both output and continuity are difficult to control. In such cases directly employed labour may be more versatile and adaptable.

Double or treble sub-letting of the work may occasionally occur either as a deliberate policy of the sub-contractor, or where more work is acquired than can be coped with. In either case, the work will probably be re-let at a lower rate, thus providing a profit or administration surcharge for the original sub-contractor. The result of such practice may often be that the actual operative working on site receives substantially less than an economic rate for individual tasks, with resultant bad feeling and possibly bad workmanship.

The builder also runs the risk of facing contra-charges or requests for daywork payments for standing time, when materials or plant are not available.

The difficulties outlined above are overcome by the majority of builders in the terms and conditions under which labour-only sub-contractors are employed. These terms and conditions are discussed in detail later in this chapter.

LOCATION OF LABOUR

Labour-only sub-contractors tend to operate in small gangs, using their home as an office or base. Wives may act as secretaries but there is often difficulty in contracting sub-contractors during normal office hours.

Builders seeking to locate and employ sub-contractors could use the following methods:

(a) Check the local press columns where sub-contractors seeking work offer their services. Similar advertisements also appear in *Yellow Pages*, published by British Telecom and other trade directories.
(b) Advertise in the local press.
(c) Advertise in the job centre.
(d) Ascertain from sub-contractors currently employed by the company if they could recommend any other sub-contractors.

Irrespective of which method is used, full details of the sub-contractor's background, including employment history, should be obtained by a requirement either to complete an application form or to attend an interview. If possible, work carried out previously by the sub-contractor should be inspected.

LABOUR-ONLY SUB-CONTRACTOR REGISTER

In view of the fact that the methods of obtaining suitable labour may be time-consuming, it is preferable and more efficient to maintain a detailed register of labour-only sub-contractors. The register could be sub-divided into trades and provide details of:

- sub-contractor's name, address and telephone number
- work-force available, such as size and number of gangs
- distance that the sub-contractor is prepared to travel
- work carried out previously and the quality and level of service provided
- tax position, daywork rate and whether registered for VAT
- public liability and employer's liability insurance

All replies received to advertisements or casual enquiries can be entered in the register. A careful note should be made against any sub-contractor used by the builder who subsequently proved to be unsatisfactory. Such a register carefully maintained in a builder's organisation will within a few years provide a detailed and comprehensive list of the majority of the sub-contract labour available in an area, with consequent improvement in efficiency in locating a suitable work-force.

APPOINTMENT OF LABOUR ONLY SUB-CONTRACTORS – TERMS AND CONDITIONS

Frequently builders appoint labour-only sub-contractors immediately following a personal interview, but it is important that work does not commence on site until the terms and conditions of employment have been agreed and confirmed in writing.

The terms and conditions should make provision for the following items.

Standard of workmanship

The sub-contractor must be advised that all work is to be executed in accordance with the relevant drawings and specification, in a proper and workmanlike manner.

Terms of reference
The sub-contractor will be expected to comply with instructions given by the general foreman, site agent or contract manager. Usually, however, working hours will be subject to negotiation.

Method of payment
The method of payment, cheque or cash, should be defined and the payment day agreed. For example, work executed will be measured on a Tuesday or Wednesday and the resultant payment made on a Thursday or Friday; that is to say, two days in arrears. Some sub-contractors, particularly when paid on the lump or a daywork basis, may expect payment on a Friday, up to and including that day, but from the builder's point of view it is preferable to keep a week in hand.

Retention
All payments to the sub-contractor should be subject to a retention of between 5% and 10%. Half of the retention would be released upon the completion of the work by the sub-contractor and the balance at the end of the 'contract' maintenance period, provided that all defects in the sub-contractor's work have been made good.

In the event of the sub-contractor failing to complete the initial work or failing to rectify any defective workmanship, the retention would not be released. Many sub-contractors agree with the builder a limit of, say, £1 000 on retention, particularly where the sub-contractor is exclusively employed by the builder at that time.

Commencement and completion dates
The sub-contractor should be advised of and have agreed to the starting and completion dates of the work for which he is responsible. The sub-contractor should also be required to co-ordinate with other trades and phase his own work to integrate with the sequence of operations in the contract programme. This may well entail a break in continuity and a return to the site at a later date.

Insurance

The sub-contractor should be required to produce evidence that he possesses both employer's liability and public liability insurance. Proof should be provided at regular intervals that the amounts insured are adequate, by presentation of the policy and proof that premiums have been paid. Alternatively the builder may prefer to provide public liability and employer's liability insurance on behalf of all sub-contractors, either without charge or by deduction of, say 1% from the payments made.

This latter approach does avoid any problems which may arise when, for example following a public liability claim, the contractor's insurance company claims reimbursement from either the sub-contractor or his insurance company. In addition, not only are the employees of the sub-contractor covered for employer's liability but also the sub-contractor himself.

Tax deduction scheme

The sub-contractor must produce a current 714 tax certificate before payments are made without deduction of tax. (The tax deduction scheme is discussed in detail later in this chapter.)

Unloading materials

Usually it will be the sub-contractor's responsibility to take delivery of, check, unload, stack and protect the material which he fixes. The sub-contractor may also be required to unload the materials required for other trades where the relevant operatives are not on site. Time taken in unloading should be recorded by the foreman and paid at the agreed daywork rate.

Plant and scaffolding

Responsibility should be defined for the provision of tools, plant and equipment and the supply and erection of scaffolding, and the terms and conditions of use of standing scaffolding, site huts and general amenities.

Sub-letting

The sub-contractor should not be permitted to sub-let the work as a whole, or any part of it, without the written consent of the builder.

Contra-charges

Contra-charges may arise against the sub-contractor as a result of:

- damage to materials, plant or completed work
- damage caused to the work of other trades
- faulty workmanship which the sub-contractor fails to rectify
- delays to the contract programme which may result, for example, in increased plant hire charges or claims by the client, against the builder, for liquidated damages
- excessive wastage of materials through negligence irrespective of whether such wastage is direct or indirect (see Chapter 5).

The sub-contractor may also have claims against the builder, for example for standing time where materials or plant are not available. Such claims may be excluded where they arise from circumstances outside the builder's control.

Safety, health and welfare

The sub-contractor should be required to maintain safe working conditions on the site and to operate within the current safety legislation.

In practice the terms and conditions of employment of sub-contractors will vary from company to company and are often drafted with a substantial bias in the builder's favour.

Some companies may use the standard form of 'Labour-only sub-contract' issued by the Building Employers' Confederation, in place of or alongside their own terms and conditions.

AGREEMENT OF RATES

The rates or lump sum payments agreed with the sub-contractor are usually framed to include the sub-contractor's responsibility for the following:

- setting out (if applicable)
- provision of all necessary tools for the trade concerned to ensure the proper execution of the work
- proper care and maintenance, including cleaning on a daily basis where necessary of all tools, plant and equipment supplied by the builder
- All on-costs including:
  overtime payments

holidays with pay contributions
travelling time and expenses
Construction Industry Training Board (CITB) levy
national insurance contributions
sick pay
tool money etc.

STANDARD DESCRIPTIONS

In order to simplify the agreement of rates and subsequent measurement of work with sub-contractors, it is common practice to use methods of measurements which conform neither with the bills of quantities nor with the standard method of measurement of building work.

Builders frequently devise standard descriptions which are omnibus and include most labour items. For example, brickwork for residential development will usually comprise:

(a) 100 mm concrete blockwork in foundations – rate per sq m. (This rate will include mixing mortar, building in lintels over pipes and services and damp-proof course.) Any different thickness of blockwork or hollow blocks would have a different rate.

(b) 100 mm thermal blockwork in superstructure – rate per sq m. (This rate will include building in door and window frames, building in lintels, forming cavities and fixing ties, closing cavities including vertical damp-proof course, building in joists or joist hangers and erecting any necessary scaffolding. The same rate will usually be applied both to blockwork in partitions and cavity walls.)

(c) Common brickwork – rate per 1000 bricks laid. (This rate will include all labour items, i.e. fair face and piers.)

(d) Facing brickwork – rate per 1000 bricks laid. (This rate will include building in door and window frames, pointing and fair face, and similar labours to those included in the rate for thermal blockwork.)

(e) Bedding wall plates – rate per linear m or alternatively a lump sum item. It is also possible that the bedding of the wall plate may be included with (b) or (c) above.

(f) Daywork rate – per hour. (This rate will be applied when difficulty is experienced in agreeing measured rates, for example time spent unloading materials, adjusting scaffolding for use by other trades and reinstating any work damaged by others.)

Due to the fact that the sub-contractor when paid on a piecework basis achieves a relatively high hourly rate, most sub-contractors either negotiate an equivalent daywork rate per hour or resist working on daywork and agree rates or lump sums for the particular work involved. Equally, the builder is usually anxious to keep daywork rates low and avoid daywork if possible.

The sub-contractor when agreeing rates with the builder will take account of the complexity of the work, the amount of repetition involved and the market conditions.

Similar omnibus rates may be used in other trades – groundwork, carpentry and joinery, etc. Some builders and sub-contractors, however, retain the bill of quantities as the basis of agreeing rates.

METHODS OF AGREEING RATES

The agreement of rates with sub-contractors may be undertaken using the following alternative methods or combinations thereof, where appropriate:

(a) A photocopied extract from the unpriced bill of quantities or internal take off is forwarded to the sub-contractor for pricing.

(b) A blank copy of the builder's standard descriptions of work (i.e. omnibus and not based on the Standard Method of Measurement) is forwarded to the sub-contractors for pricing.

(c) A priced schedule of the builder's standard description of work is forwarded to the sub-contractor with the option that the rates are fixed by the builder and the sub-contractor has no opportunity to negotiate, or the sub-contractor is given the opportunity to quote a percentage surcharge or discount off the complete schedule or individual rates.

(d) Each rate is individually negotiated between the sub-contractor and the builder.

When comparing quotations from sub-contractors, care is necessary to assess the relationship between different items, as discussed in the section on labour and material sub-contractors later in this chapter.

STANDARDISATION OF RATES

Where the builder employs more than one sub-contractor of the same trade on the same site or within a confined geographical area, there will be a tendency for the builder to fix the rates to avoid any conflict or ill-feeling between the various sub-contractors employed.

STRUCTURE OF LABOUR-ONLY SUB-CONTRACT GANGS

The majority of labour-only sub-contract gangs are limited in size to a maximum of six persons. Irrespective of which method is used by the gang leader to divide payments, problems will arise if the trade skill and quality and quantity of output of the gang members is mismatched. If members do not achieve a similar output, resentment will arise if the payment is divided equally at the end of the week. Such pressures can be alleviated if gang sizes are kept small and either the gang members are assembled in groups of similar ability, or demarcation is identified, recognised and accepted by all gang members.

Either the gang leader (or leaders, where they are in partnership) will employ the gang members direct, paying national insurance contributions and operating the PAYE scheme, or more commonly, each gang member will be employed on a sub-contract basis. The method used by the gang leader to divide payments will vary as follows:

(a) The money will be divided equally between all gang members.
(b) Gang members will be employed at a fixed hourly, daily or weekly rate, whether direct or sub-contract, and the gang leader retains the balance as his own income. Any gang member who regularly fails to break even or achieve a surplus would be laid off.
(c) The gang leader may agree rates with the builder and pay lower rates to other gang members, or alternatively sub-let the work at lower rates to other independent gangs. When rates are discounted in this way by substantial amounts, bad feeling and discontent may well develop on the site. As mentioned earlier in this chapter, builders should if possible eliminate sub-letting to independent gangs.
(d) The gang may be constituted of two or three core members with other tradesmen or labourers employed either on daywork or discounted rates. The gang leader will share the balance of the payment either equally or by an agreed formula between the core members.

Occasionally labour-only sub-contractors develop into large organisations or agencies with a significant control of a trade in a geographical area. Usually such organisations are built up of a multiplicity of smaller gangs. Advantages to the individual sub-contractors from continuity of work and reduced administration offset the marginal discount in the rates, to cover the overheads of the agency. Moreover, these larger organisations are better equipped to arrange for training of apprentices.

MEASUREMENT OF WORK EXECUTED BY LABOUR-ONLY SUB-CONTRACTORS

The appointment of sub-contractors and agreement of rates may be the individual or joint responsibility of the contract manager, surveyor or buyer, depending on the builder's management structure. The measurement and valuation of work completed each week, however, will usually be the responsibility of the project surveyor, with the contract manager, chief surveyor or a director authorising the payment to the sub-contractor.

Measurement of sub-contractor's work is a difficult and laborious task and management controls are necessary to ensure that work is accurately measured and valued and that the surveyor has sufficient time to achieve these objectives.

METHOD OF MEASUREMENT

Outlined below are methods of measurement commonly used by surveyors; it should be noted that some methods have more merit than others.

(a) The sub-contractor is encouraged to measure the work himself and submit a detailed account to the surveyor together with any daywork sheets signed by the general foreman. The surveyor should, but may not, check these payment requests, depending on time, ability or perseverance.

(b) The surveyor measures on site the work executed by the sub-contractor each week and prepares a weekly account. Weekly accounts should be abstracted to produce a final account.

(c) The surveyor takes off the quantities from the drawing or, less satisfactorily, extracts the relevant figures from the bill of quantities in order to calculate the total value of the sub-contract work. Stage or interim payments are then made each week to the sub-contractor and the surveyor will make any necessary remeasurement and adjust the final quantities and payment accordingly. Larger building companies may have reduced this operation to a form-filling exercise, particularly on repetitive projects, for example housing.

(d) The surveyor makes stage payments based on approximate quantities or related to the number of men employed, and accurately measures and values the work either on completion of relevant sections of the work or at regular monthly intervals.

PURPOSE OF MEASUREMENT

Whichever method of measurement is adopted it is essential that the surveyor achieves the following:

(a) That the weekly measurement is sufficiently accurate to maintain a good working relationship with the sub-contractor.
(b) That no overlap of measurement occurs, with the consequential payment of the sub-contractor twice for the same operation. Using method (b) above this will be all too easy, particularly on a large and complicated project.
(c) That the total measured quantity and total cost of each individual item can be clearly identified and that a detailed final account is available for each sub-contractor.
(d) That care is taken to ensure that overpayments do not occur, particularly when using method (c) above.
(e) That, when a sub-contractor will be on site for an extensive period, detailed interim accounts are prepared at monthly intervals.
(f) That daywork hours for such items as unloading are accurately checked. Problems may arise where the foreman is bribed or negligent and excessive hours are claimed by the sub-contractor. The surveyor can easily assess the relationship between earnings on measured work and daywork, in order to verify the daywork hours, provided he is aware of the total hours worked each week.

It should be noted that from time to time sub-contractors may be employed on 'the lump' (a fixed sum per day for each man employed). In this case the surveyor should be careful to check for 'dead men', e.g. 23 men claimed for, but only 22 on the site, the payment for the 'dead man' being divided between the sub-contractor and the site management.

MANAGEMENT CONTROLS

It will be apparent that the surveyor could be negligent, overworked, dishonest or incompetent, and therefore fail to achieve accurate measurement. Moreover, surveyors are sometimes pressurised by the sub-contractor to overpay, particularly when output has been restricted during adverse weather conditions.

It is therefore essential that the chief surveyor, director, or other member of the management team maintains a watching brief to monitor the accuracy of measurement and to ensure that the surveyor has sufficient time to achieve his objectives.

PAYMENT CERTIFICATES
For costing and accounting purposes it is usual for payments to be supported by a payment certificate or a standard format. The certificate should show:

- the gross payment to date
- deduction for retention to date
- deduction for insurance, CITB levy, etc.
- previous payments
- net payment for period

(See Chapter 9, Costing.)

LABOUR AND MATERIAL SUB-CONTRACTORS

The labour and material sub-contractor is a sub-contractor who supplies not only labour, but also all the necessary materials to complete the work. The provision of plant and scaffolding will usually be subject to negotiation and may be supplied by either the builder or the sub-contractor. Such sub-contracting firms are diverse in structure and vary in size from the one man painter and decorator to the public company with a turnover in excess of the majority of main contractors.

The use of labour and material sub-contractors is common practice in the building industry, because:

(a) The builder does not possess the necessary expert technical knowledge and specialist skills in certain aspects of the construction process.
(b) Demand for specialist work may be of an intermittent nature and the builder may have difficulty in providing the operatives with continuity of work. Equally, demand for the specialist work-force may arise simultaneously on separate projects.
(c) Competition between sub-contractors tends to reduce the cost to the builder. In addition, the sub-contractor can achieve both economies of scale and improved efficiency from maximum use of both plant and labour.
(d) The builder has the advantages of greater control over cost and reduced administration.

Traditionally, certain specialist work such as asphalt and felt roofing, heating and ventilating, shopfitting, lift installations and piling are usually sub-let by builders. Other work of a less specialist nature – plumbing, plastering, roofing, flooring and wall tiling, painting and decorating – may be undertaken by the builder's own work-force, labour-only sub-contractors or labour and material sub-contractors.

Where construction work is executed under a formal contract the builder may require the written approval of the architect before any part of the work can be sub-let.

QUOTATIONS

The procedures used to obtain quotations are similar to those outlined in Chapter 5, relating to the purchase of materials.

The majority of sub-contractors either price an extract from the bill of quantities or prepare an estimate from the drawings and specification.

When comparing quotations a straightforward financial check is inadequate. Frequently relationships exist between rates. For example, when pricing excavation, removal and disposal of excavated material on site, the sub-contractor may make enquiries regarding the ultimate disposal of the spoil and in the process identify possible variations to the stated quantities. The rates can then be adjusted to produce an apparently low price overall which will benefit the sub-contractor on remeasurement.

It will also be difficult to compare quotations where items have been priced without the relevant quantities. Moreover, care must be taken to ensure that the sub-contractor does not front-end load the pricing of the work, particularly where the sub-contract period is prolonged or intermittent.

Before a sub-contractor's quotation is accepted and an appointment is made, the builder must establish that:

(a) The quality of workmanship achieved by the sub-contractor on previous contracts is satisfactory.
(b) The sub-contractor can meet the requirements of the contract programme.
(c) The sub-contractor has made adequate provision for public liability and employers' liability insurance.
(d) The terms and conditions of the sub-contract are clearly defined and agreed in writing.

MEASUREMENT AND PAYMENT

The builder's surveyor will normally remeasure the work executed by labour and material sub-contractors, who may agree the measurements on site or alternatively submit a formal invoice or payment request for the builder's surveyor to check and approve. The payment details will usually be entered on a certificate with provision for deduction of previous payments and retention.

Payments to the smaller labour and material sub-contractor may be included with the weekly labour-only payments whereas the larger companies may be paid monthly or on a monthly account basis with or without cash discount.

NAMED SUB-CONTRACTORS

Under the term of JCT 80 the contractor is obliged to obtain the written consent of the architect to sub-let any part of the contract works. Consent should not be unreasonably withheld and sub-contractors so employed are referred to as domestic sub-contractors. Frequently on smaller contracts, builders do not formally obtain consent and assume that it would be granted.

The employer, or the architect on his behalf, for certain sections of a contract may provide a list, in or attached to the contract bills, of at least three sub-contractors from which the builder must select one able and willing to carry out the respective work. Such sub-contractors, although once appointed are treated in every way as domestic sub-contractors, are referred to as named sub-contractors.

If the list of those sub-contractors willing to undertake the work is less than three in number, either the employer or the contractor may add additional names to the list. Alternatively the contractor may sub-let the work to a domestic sub-contractor with the written consent of the architect.

In any event at any time prior to the execution of a binding sub-contract agreement, either the employer or the contractor may add additional sub-contractors to the list. In each and every case the consent of either party to the contract should not be unreasonably withheld.

NOMINATED SUB-CONTRACTORS

The architect may choose to obtain quotations for certain areas of the work from specialist labour and material sub-contractors, under JCT 80, who will be known as nominated sub-contractors. The builder will subsequently be instructed by the architect to place an order with the firm selected and enter into a formal sub-contract agreement.

Usually a prime cost sum, together with a description of the sub-contract work, is included in the bill of quantities, and the builder is given the opportunity to price for profit, general attendance and special attendance, as defined in clause B9 of the 6th edition of the *Standard Method of Measurement*. The builder is also entitled to a cash discount of $2\frac{1}{2}\%$ on the total value of the nominated sub-contractor's account.

The term 'prime cost sum' is defined in SMM6 as 'a sum provided for work or services to be executed by a nominated sub-contractor, a statutory authority or a public undertaking or for materials or goods to be obtained from a nominated supplier'. The term 'provisional sum' is defined as 'a sum provided for work or for costs which cannot be entirely foreseen, defined or detailed at the time the tendering documents are issued'.

The relationship between the architect, builder and nominated sub-contractor will be defined in the terms of both the main contract and the sub-contract agreement. Under the terms of JCT 80:

(a) The contractor has the right to raise reasonable objections against the use of a particular nominated sub-contractor.

(b) The contractor has the obligation to pay the nominated sub-contractor the sums directed by the architect and included in the interim certificate, less the agreed retention and cash discount. The nominated sub-contractor must be paid within 17 days of the date of issue of the certificate. Theoretically, under clause 30.1.1.1, the contractor is entitled to payment by the client within 14 days from the date of issue of each interim certificate, thus providing three days of grace.

(c) The contractor is obliged under clause 35.13.3, before the issue of each interim certificate, to provide the client's quantity surveyor with reasonable proof that the payments authorised to nominated sub-contractors in the previous certificate have been made. In the event of the contractor failing to provide the necessary proof of payment where he is able to do so, the employer has the right to pay the sub-contractor direct and deduct the equivalent sums from other payments to the contractor.

The contractor is often in a difficult position, when payments to the nominated sub-contractor are only due to be made immediately prior to the next valuation, and insufficient time remains for receipts to be obtained. The client's quantity surveyor may co-operate, particularly where the relationship with the contractor is well established, either by accepting receipts one month in arrears, subject to the payment being made on time, or by a telephone enquiry to the nominated sub-contractors concerned to obtain verbal confirmation that payment has been made.

(d) The contractor has the possible opportunity to tender, with the approval of the architect, for work which is subject to a prime cost sum, provided the contractor directly carries out such work in the ordinary course of his business. If the contractor's tender is accepted, he will not be able to sub-let the work to a domestic sub-contractor without the consent of the architect.

A TAX DEDUCTION SCHEME FOR SUB-CONTRACTORS

The continuing growth in the number of sub-contractors' 'lump' labour employed in the construction industry during the 1960s and early '70s was viewed with increasing concern and suspicion by government authorities, because of the widespread avoidance of payment of both income tax and national insurance contributions. During this period contractors frequently made payments in cash and individual sub-contractors changed their names from time to time to avoid detection by Inland Revenue inspectors. Moreover, as payments were commonly made to gang leaders, the contractor was unlikely to be aware of even the names of men employed on the site. This abuse of tax legislation consequently received increasing attention and criticism from the public and was voiced in the media.

The Finance (No 2) Act 1975 made sweeping changes to the law and placed both the contractor and sub-contractor in such a position that tax avoidance was virtually halted. A few instances of forged documentation and fraud have subsequently occurred, but only to a limited extent.

In essence the result of this change was to ensure that when a contractor made a payment to a sub-contractor holding a tax certificate issued by the Inland Revenue, the sub-contractor could be paid in full. If on the other hand the sub-contractor did *not* hold a tax certificate, the contractor must deduct tax from the payment and pass the deduction over to the Inland Revenue.

The sub-contractor either employs the gang members direct, in which case the PAYE scheme will operate, or the members of the gang are employed as sub-contractors and the tax deduction scheme will operate with the gang leader functioning as both a sub-contractor and a contractor.

SUB-CONTRACTORS TAX CERTIFICATES

The purpose of the tax certificate is to permit a sub-contractor to receive payment from a builder without deduction of tax. Each sub-contractor holding a certificate will subsequently be assessed for tax and pay the Inland Revenue direct.

There are four types of tax certificate:

Form 714 I   The I certificate is issued to an individual in business on his own.

Form 714 S   The S certificate is a special certificate for sub-contractors whose history of continuous employment is too short to qualify for Form 714 I. The sub-contractor is restricted to a maximum payment which may be received without deduction of tax.

Form 714 P   The P certificate is issued to an individual who is a partner in a firm, and to certain companies (usually new companies whose financial background is unknown to the Inland Revenue).

Form 714 C   The C certificate is issued to certain other companies. In this case more than one certificate may be issued and marked 'original' or 'official copy'.

The tax certificate will show:

- the name of the individual or company
- the national insurance number of the individual or, if a company, the registration number
- the signature of the individual or the signature of the company secretary
- the date of expiry and the certificate number
- the I, S and P certificates also show a photograph of the holder

PROCEDURE WHEN PAYMENT IS MADE TO A SUB-CONTRACTOR HOLDING A TAX CERTIFICATE

Before payment is made to a sub-contractor without deduction for tax, the builder must satisfy himself that the tax certificate is valid. A sub-contractor who holds an I, S or P certificate must present the actual certificate to the builder for inspection.

A sub-contractor who holds a C certificate may choose to present to the builder the 'original' and 'official copy' or alternatively a special 'certifying document' confirming that the company holds a tax certificate.

Figure 6.1 identifies the types of certificates and shows the checks that the builder should make to establish their authenticity.

Once the contractor is satisfied that a sub-contractor holds a valid certificate no further inspection is necessary unless:

(a) The date of expiry, which should have been noted in the builder's records, has passed.
(b) The builder has reason to doubt that the certificate is still valid.

On receiving payment without deduction from a builder the sub-contractor holding an I, S or P certificate *must* within seven days give the builder a completed voucher, Form 715. Where the payment is in cash, the voucher should be provided at the time of payment. A sub-contractor who fails to supply the 715 voucher may have his certificate withdrawn by the Inland Revenue.

The builder is also under obligation to:

(a) Make every reasonable effort to obtain fully completed 715 vouchers from sub-contractors.
(b) Forward batches of vouchers to the Inland Revenue at weekly intervals.
(c) Ensure that no voucher is retained for a longer period than 14 days from receipt.
(d) Keep records of all payments made and make annual returns to the Inland Revenue.

Sub-contractors holding a C certificate are not required to provide 715 vouchers but the builder should normally make all payments to the sub-contractor by cheque.

PROCEDURE WHEN PAYMENT IS MADE TO A SUB-CONTRACTOR WHO DOES NOT HOLD A TAX CERTIFICATE

A builder making a payment to a sub-contractor who does not have a certificate must make a deduction from the payment for tax.

The net cost of any materials supplied by the sub-contractor, and, by concession, the CITB levy, may be excluded from the gross payment before tax deduction is calculated (NB The current deduction rate is 27%.)

The builder is also under obligation to:

(a) Provide the sub-contractor with Form SC60 to verify that tax has been deducted from payments made.

Sub-Contractor's Tax Certificate
Contractors Checking Guide

1. See the actual Sub-contractor's Tax Certificate, NOT a photocopy. It will look like one of the following:

I CERTIFICATE
P CERTIFICATE
S CERTIFICATE

————Optional————

2. Make the following checks:-
   a. Does the certificate bear the photograph of the person presenting it?
   b. Is the certificate still in date?
   c. Do you know the sub-contractor? If not, ask for a specimen signature and check it against the signature on the certificate (on reverse of 714S).
3. If there is still some doubt about the sub-contractor's identity, ask for further evidence of identification. Are you satisfied he is the person described in the certificate? If not satisfied, you must make the deduction.
4. If you are now satisfied, having carried out the checks, that the sub-contractor is the authorised user of a 714I or 714P certificate, you can pay him without the deduction but obtain a fully completed voucher (form 715) for every payment as soon as possible.

   If you are satisfied that the sub-contractor is the authorised user of a 714S certificate, you can pay him without deduction ONLY:-
   a. up to the limit shown on the voucher (form 715S), AND
   b. if you obtain a fully completed voucher (form 715S) on or before making the payment.

Either sub-contractor presents a

C CERTIFICATE

or sub-contractor company gives special CERTIFYING DOCUMENT

signed by its secretary or director.

1. Do you recognise the certificate as one issued by the Inland Revenue?
2. Is the certificate still in date?
3. Is this the name of the company which is your sub-contractor?
4. Is the certificate presented by an authorised representative of the company? If in doubt, or if he asks to be paid in cash, telephone company secretary.
5. If you are now satisfied that the certificate is presented by an authorised representative of the company and that it is valid, pay without deduction. If NOT, make the deduction.

1. Does the certifying document state that the sub-contractor company is the user of a valid C certificate and show
   a. its name?
   b. its address and company number?
   c. the number of its C certificate and the address of the Inspector who issued it?
   d. the date of the expiry of the certificate?
   e. details of the special bank account or accounts?
2. Is the payment due under a contract in writing?
3. Is the certificate still in date?
4. If the answer to all these questions is YES, make payment without deduction (see paragraph 112 of IR Booklet 14/15 (1982). DO NOT pay in cash.
5. If in doubt about the authenticity of the certifying document, see paragraphs 108 to 110 of the Inland Revenue booklet 'Construction Industry: Tax Deduction Scheme.'

REMEMBER: IF YOU FAIL TO MAKE THESE CHECKS YOU MAY BE LIABLE TO PAY THE TAX YOURSELF

Fig. 6.1 Sub-contractor's tax certificate checking guide

(b) Pay over to the Inland Revenue each month all amounts that should have been deducted from uncertified sub-contractors' payments. These payments must be made irrespective of whether or not tax has been deducted from the sub-contractors' payments.

(c) Send an annual return to the Inland Revenue immediately after 5 April each year, listing all the uncertified sub-contractors and the total amount deducted.

Such detailed procedures required to be operated by builders involve an equivalent, if not greater, cost to administer than the traditional PAYE scheme for directly employed labour.

The private householder having work done to his own property is not required to make deductions from any payments he may make to sub-contractors. There are, therefore, a few sub-contractors who may choose to work exclusively in this sector and continue to avoid detection by the Inland Revenue.

In general, however, the scheme has been successful and has achieved the purposes for which it was instituted.

DIRECTLY EMPLOYED LABOUR

The analysis of the advantages and disadvantages of using labour-only sub-contractors, outlined earlier in this chapter, is of course of relevance when examining the use of directly employed labour. Both management and operatives are locked into a closer relationship, with both mutual benefits and disadvantages.

On-costs, which have to be added to the basic labour rate, are continually rising and the breakdown of labour costs in price books such as *Griffiths, Spon's* or *Laxton*, shows a percentage addition of approximately 85%.

DISADVANTAGES

For the builder the most significant disadvantages created by the employment of directly employed labour are the need to:

(a) Create incentive or motivation which will induce the operative to achieve a production rate that will equal or better the tender or estimate.

(b) Counteract the tendency for the most able craftsmen preferring to work as sub-contractors.

(c) Maintain continuity of employment throughout the working day and between one project and the next.
(d) Motivate and encourage the directly employed labour force who are often given the less straightforward, more difficult or dirty tasks which have been rejected by labour-only sub-contractors.

ADVANTAGES

The advantages of using directly employed labour are as follows:

(a) It provides management with flexibility, particularly in coping with crisis labour demands and small works.
(b) The development of craft and company pride and the opportunity for the directly employed operative to achieve promotion to the salaried staff.

METHOD OF PAYMENT

There are three basic methods of payment to directly employed labour. First, a calculation based on the wage rates laid down by the National Joint Council for the Building Industry (NJCBI) in the national working rules. These provide for a rate per hour, a guaranteed minimum bonus and joint board supplement to provide a basic rate. Payment on this basis is related to hours of attendance and does not encourage operatives to increase their productivity.

Second, a guaranteed bonus or plus rate in addition to the basic rate. Management may monitor performance and, in times of recession when building labour is freely available, lay off operatives who fail to achieve the output required. When the industry is expanding and labour is scarce, management will obviously have less control over productivity.

Third, an incentive scheme which in addition to the basic rate aims to offer a monetary reward in exchange for increased productivity from the operative.

INCENTIVE SCHEMES

Management in the building industry has devised many, varied types of financial incentive. In each case the primary objective has been to increase both earnings and productivity. The basic methods are profit sharing, partnership schemes and earned bonus.

Profit sharing

The profit of the company is partially shared with employees and a payment made once or twice a year. The basis on which this takes place must be defined and easily understood. A common method is to operate a points system where the operative is awarded points related, for example, to his trade, position and length of service. This type of scheme may also include office staff. Success in operation will depend on the goodwill of the labour force as there is a collective rather than personal incentive. A disadvantage of this type of incentive scheme is that in a 'bad' year the operative may work hard but, in the absence of profit, will receive no reward.

Partnership schemes

The company may enter into a formal agreement with its work-force to transfer a substantial percentage of gross profits each year to a trust fund. Each operative will receive a defined share of the income from the trust at regular intervals and on retirement will receive a pension or on death a grant will be paid. The various benefits will be dependent on length of service with the company.

The trust fund, with mutual agreement, may also fund residential and industrial development undertaken by the company.

Partnership incentive schemes are comparatively rare but can result in a highly motivated and dedicated work-force.

Earned bonus

Earned bonus is the most widely used form of financial incentive, because it most closely meets the objectives of an incentive scheme, which are:

(a) To provide the opportunity for increased earnings in return for increased output.
(b) To increase efficiency and reduce costs.
(c) To improve financial control.

There are many different forms of earned bonus. The basic concept is that a target for a work element is set in man hours and at the end of each week the difference between the target hours, and actual hours worked is paid as a bonus to the operative.

ESSENTIAL FEATURES OF A BONUS SCHEME

Essential features of a bonus schemes are as follows:

(a) The scheme must be easily understood by the operative.
(b) The targets set must be attainable and should represent the average output of the average operative or gang working under average conditions without loss of quality of work.
(c) Targets should be agreed in writing between management and operatives before the work commences on site. Restrospective targets will obviously be ineffective.
(d) Payments should be made at regular intervals, preferably weekly.
(e) Targets should provide for a balance between craftsmen, labourers and apprentices in the make-up of a gang.
(f) Losses accruing in one bonus period should not be offset against the bonus earned by employees in another.
(g) Penalties should be introduced for excessive wastage of materials or misuse of plant. Operatives should be advised of these penalties in advance.
(h) Safety, health and welfare regulations should be observed by both management and labour.
(i) Management must ensure that the site is well organised and materials are delivered on time. Work must be programmed to avoid delay between tasks, and instructions issued promptly. If unavoidable delays do occur the operative should be paid at the basic rate and the hours excluded from bonus calculations.
(j) If the work is defective the time spent by the operative in rectification should be included in the operational time.
(k) The basic wage should be paid strictly in accordance with the working rule agreement.
(l) The scheme should be honestly and fairly operated by both management and labour. This is perhaps the most important aspect of the integrity of any scheme.

DIFFICULTIES IN OPERATION

Preferably targets should be set for individuals where the bonus earned is directly related to personal effort. The nature of building work normally necessitates the use of a gang. The size of the gang, however, should be kept as small as possible and should not exceed six members.

The comments made earlier in this chapter covering the balance of ability and mutual interdependence of sub-contract gangs apply equally to directly employed labour gangs.

Wherever possible all work should be subject to bonus. This will avoid the inclination of either management or labour to wrongly allocate the time spent on work attracting bonus to other non-bonus operations. Moreover, there may well be reluctance or bad feeling when the operative or gang is obliged to undertake work without bonus.

Increased productivity is equally the responsibility of management, who must ensure that materials, plant and scaffolding are available and in the right location, adequate instructions are given on time, the work place is prepared and the programme of work for other trades correlated and integrated.

THE BONUS TARGET

Setting targets that are fair and reasonable to both management and labour is perhaps the most formidable difficulty in operating a bonus scheme.

The target is best expressed in hours rather than in money terms. The operative adapts to the idea of saving time and bonus calculations are greatly simplified. Moreover, time targets do not need recalculation when the basic rate is changed and they can also be utilised for planning and programming of the work.

In order to set the bonus targets it is necessary to establish the quantity of work to be done, the method of construction, and the calulation of the relevant man hours necessary to complete the task.

Quantity of work

The quantity of work can be extracted from the bill of quantities if available. Alternatively the quantities can be taken off from the drawings or extracted from the builder's estimate.

The bill of quantities may be of limited use because many items of the work will be presented in a summarised form. For example, an item billed as '100 sq m half brick wall in facings' may represent work in different locations on site, to be executed at various times. Even when the work can be executed in one operation it may prove beneficial to identify stage targets, for example first lift or second lift on brickwork. Elemental, annotated or operational bills may be of greater value but the most reliable system is to take off the quantities from the drawings. This take off could also be utilised by the buying, planning and surveying departments.

The extent of the work to be included in the bonus target should be geared to provide the operative with the maximum incentive. If the target time is protracted the operative may have difficulty in pacing and measuring output, and lose enthusiasm.

Work content should result in target times of preferably two to three days and definitely not more than five days. The smaller the task the greater the incentive. Exceptions could be made where work is of a repetitive nature, such as residential housing. Targets can, in such cases, be set on a unit basis because the tradesmen can utilise previous experience as a guide.

Method of construction

Contract management in planning and programming the work will decide the method of construction. Work content will be affected by these decisions, particularly in relation to the use of plant. For example, concrete could be site mixed and placed by hand, or supplied ready mixed and placed by hand or by using a hoist, or tower crane or pump. In each case the work content would be dissimilar, different sized gangs would be necessary to complete the task efficiently and continuity of work could be affected. Planning and programming are, therefore, closely interrelated with the assessment of the work content.

Work values

The estimates of operational time – the actual bonus target – will be expressed in individual or gang hours, for example:

$$\frac{\text{Quantity of work} \times \text{Labour constant}}{\text{Gang size}} = \text{Target hours}$$

Labour constant

The labour constant used to calculate the bonus target must represent fairly the average output of the average operative, working under average conditions.

The constant to be applied may be obtained from:

(a) The breakdown of the rate used by the estimator in producing the tender.
(b) Standard reference books of labour constants.
(c) Records kept by management, work-study officers or bonus surveyors for similar work on previous contracts.
(d) Personal assessment by management based on knowledge and experience.

Whichever method is used, it is essential that where doubts exist management should monitor the output of the work-force before finalising the target.

It may also be necessary to adjust accepted labour constants to the actual circumstances of the job. For example, the estimator and standard price books use a common labour constant for brickwork; in practice the labour constant could be adjusted to provide different targets for, say, work at ground level and work in the gables.

The labour constant should provide for meal breaks, weather, site conditions, time spent receiving and understanding instructions, locating materials and plant, measuring and setting out, maintenance of plant, clearing up, and observance of safety regulations.

The constant should be adjusted to reflect fairly the nature of the actual work involved. For example, the quality, repetition within or between tasks, working environment, relationship with other trades, and the method of execution of the work. The labour constant should also give the operatives of different gangs or trades equal opportunity to earn a similar percentage bonus.

Work and method study is essential in the successful operation of a bonus scheme.

MEASUREMENT AND PAYMENT OF BONUS

Most builders operating incentive schemes employ a bonus surveyor to measure and calculate the bonus paid to each operative.

The hours saved against the target set are not necessarily paid in full. Some firms introduce a percentage factor into the calculation and only pay between 50% and 90% of the hours saved. Where percentage factors are introduced the operative will receive a disproportionate amount of bonus for the effort involved and will, therefore, have a reduced incentive to increase his productivity.

It may prove acceptable for management to retain a small percentage, say 10%, as a reserve. This reserve will be used to offset any losses which may arise for each trade or gang during the progress of the contract. The balance remaining on completion will be shared out amongst the operatives concerned.

A typical simplified bonus calculation would, therefore, be as follows:

Total hours worked		40
Target hours for completed operations	50	
Actual hours booked	35	
Hours saved	15	
% bonus payable (90%)		$13\frac{1}{2}$
Hours paid		$53\frac{1}{2}$

The bonus surveyor would make adjustments for partially completed work and time spent working in different gangs.

Hours spent waiting for instructions, wet time, and working on unbonussed operations would be included in total hours worked, but not set against the target hours.

It will be immediately apparent that the bonus surveyor or site management responsible for completing records of hours worked must be honest, fair, competent and trusted by both management and labour for the incentive scheme to work satisfactorily.

If possible, bonus should be paid in the week in which it is earned and certainly not later than the following week.

NON-FINANCIAL INCENTIVES

The directly employed building operative may be motivated by factors other than money incentives. Many craftsmen take pride in a good job well done and often friendly rivalry develops between them to achieve personal, rather than financial, objectives. Working conditions, job security and social relationships in the work-place are also important.

CONCLUSION

- Incentive schemes do not compare favourably with the 'piece-work' system most commonly used in the payment of labour-only sub-contractors. The sub-contractor only receives payment in direct relationship to his productivity, thus 'no work, no earnings'.
- Management when using directly employed labour may have more opportunity to conceal its own inefficiency. Problems with planning and programming, delays in delivery of materials or plant, and double-handling, are all less likely to be identified. In the face of such difficulties the labour-only sub-contractor will withdraw his labour or raise a contra-account to cover any loss he sustains.
- When directly employed labour is used on an incentive scheme, losses in one bonus period cannot be offset against gains in other periods. However, where a bonus reserve has been created, this problem may be mitigated.
- In a 'bad' week, directly employed labour used under the terms of an incentive scheme may fail to qualify for the usual level of bonus payment. In order to maintain morale, or avoid loss of the labour force, or through other motives, management may make an ex-gratia or 'policy' bonus payment, thus destroying the cost-effectiveness of the scheme.

FEED BACK TO MANAGEMENT

In the smaller company the feedback of labour costs to management is frequently neglected. There can be substantial pressure on the builder's surveyor in locating and engaging labour and in the measurement of bonus, or labour-only sub-contractors' work, on a weekly basis. The surveyor may fail to abstract the available data into a suitable form to compare directly with the bill of quantities or estimate. Equally, the estimator may have insufficient time or resources to provide a breakdown of the estimate.

Nevertheless, the feedback of accurate quantity and cost data to management is essential for accurate cost control. The larger company may well use standard formats and their systems will provide:

(a) A breakdown of the bill of quantities or original estimate for each priced item into labour, material, plant, overheads and profit.
(b) A take off of the quantities from the drawings to provide a breakdown and check of the quantities in the bill. The take off will be annotated with site location references.
(c) Quantities from the annotated take off must be abstracted to correspond with the basis on which the work is sub-let or bonussed. In certain trades, e.g. brickwork, square metres would be expressed in thousands of bricks and labour items included to provide a true comparison of cost.
(d) The remeasured quantity and rates would be abstracted each week and on completion compared with the breakdown provided by the estimator. This feedback would highlight differences in both quantities and labour rates.

The information provided will assist the surveyor in the preparation of the final account. A system of this nature will also be valuable backup to clarify and amplify the more general indication of profit or loss on work-in-progress produced by the cost value reconciliation process, as discussed in Chapter 11.

It is probably unwise to feed results direct to the estimating department. Management should first examine the data produced to ascertain whether any variance from the breakdown is due to site conditions or mismanagement.

TRAINING

Between 1974 and 1985 the number of trainees in the construction industry fell from 83.7 thousand to 49.2 thousand. This fall in operative trainees has primarily been due to the reduced demand following the recession in construction activity since the property collapse of 1973.

The growth of labour-only sub-contracting has also resulted in reduced opportunities for training. Many sub-contractors are unwilling to accept the responsibility and initial liability of training apprentices. A few of the larger labour-only organisations, on the other hand, have made substantial provision for training, but such instances are comparatively rare.

The 'chancer' or 'bodger' in the building industry has in recent years become more of a problem. Bricklayers' labourers, for example, may by endeavour acquire some of the necessary skills to 'get by' but, without proper training or instruction in the finer points of their craft, may prove to be a liability to the industry. The growth of Youth Training Schemes and other government schemes may also prove to be short-term expedients. Operatives may be produced who are, to quote Mr Leslie Kemp, the 1983 chairman of the CITB, 'general handymen, expensively trained by the taxpayer, turning up on site and giving the services of a jack-of-all-trades and master of none'.

The CITB, which was established under the Industrial Training Act of 1964, has a firm commitment to training in industry. The Board is funded by an annual levy on builders and sub-contractors. It assists in training by providing grants to aid apprentices and training schemes.

7 Development Land

INTRODUCTION

The contractor is always faced with the problem of getting work and maintaining turnover. The continuity of a successful outcome of the tendering process is the springboard of a company's future growth and prosperity.

The builder engaged in development, however, is confronted with a similar, perhaps even greater, hurdle in the location, inspection, investigation and purchase of land suitable for residential development, which is fraught with difficulties and pitfalls. If mistakes are made they can be costly, particularly when dealing with large sites. This chapter approaches the problem from the standpoint of the developer/builder, and identifies the procedures to be adopted in locating land, investigating its development potential, and submitting a suitable offer.

Privately owned land tends to move to its most profitable use but frequently obstacles, either physical or human, delay such movements, particularly where it is necessary to assemble adjacent parcels of land to form a viable development site. The developer or his land buyer should act as the catalyst in such situations. Sites and their related buildings may alternate in use over the years under economic pressure to give the best possible financial return, subject to planning and other restrictions. At any given point in time, however, such sites may offer latent potential to the developer. Land is in fixed supply, and what is considered uneconomic to develop in one period may prove profitable at a later date. In the early '70s, with continual inflation in land prices, development profits were guaranteed; indeed it was difficult to differentiate between development and construction profit on the one hand and inflation in land value on the other. Since that time, however, greater care has been needed in accurately assessing land value, development and construction costs and profits.

The developer is also faced with the problem of determining the optimum size of his land bank. Land is both stock-in-trade and a financial liability, particularly with the fluctuating rates of interest which are currently prevalent. It is considered that an ideal land bank will vary between a minimum of three years' and a maximum of five years' stock.

While a detailed consideration is outside the scope of this book, it is important to appreciate the relationship between the built environment and the demand for new housing. The second-hand sector of the housing market represents over 90% of all house sales. The market price of the second-hand house, therefore, to a large extent determines the sale price of new houses and hence land values. House building has declined in Great Britain from 350 392 per annum in 1970 to 198 400 per annum in 1984. The stock of dwellings has increased from 19.415 million in 1973 to 21.494 million in 1983, while population in the same period has grown from 54.671 million to 54.804 million.

The number of households, however, is the key statistic relating to housing demand. Household formation is increasing at a faster rate than the population as a result of smaller families, increase in the divorce rate and longer life spans. As a consequence, much of the demand for new housing is now concentrated in starter homes for single people or married couples, and one- or two-bedroom units suitable for retirement. There is a crude housing surplus of approximately 500 000 dwellings over households, but many of these houses are second homes, or are unfit for occupation, or in areas of high unemployment, where workers have migrated to other parts of the country. Some surplus housing, however, is required to permit normal movement of the population.

The key issues in bringing land forward for development are concerned with planning approval, infrastructure and the provision of the necessary services. Each of these areas will be examimed in this chapter.

CLASSIFICATION OF LAND AND THE BUILT ENVIRONMENT

Land can be classified in a variety of ways, but perhaps the two most basic classifications are concerned first with its legal status and secondly, and of equal importance, its status under the Town and Country Planning Acts.

LEGAL CLASSIFICATION
In England the ownership of land is usually either freehold or leasehold. Ownership of the freehold is defined as ownership in 'fee simple absolute

in possession' and under the Crown land held by a freeholder is in perpetuity as absolute owner. In theory the freeholder, as absolute owner, may do what he likes with his land. In practice, however, these rights may be restricted by the Planning Acts, and by easements or restrictive covenants, although the freeholder may in turn benefit from easements or restrictive covenants imposed on adjoining land.

The freeholder may separate and transfer certain rights inherent in the ownership of the fee simple absolute to another person for a fixed term of years. Such an arrangement, where the freeholder, instead of occupying the land or property himself, grants the exclusive rights of possession to another party for a defined period, in consideration of the payment of a rent, is known as leasehold. Leases may be granted for short periods of less than a year, up to 999 years. At the termination of the lease (reversion) the freeholder will regain physical possession of the land or property. The freeholder may of course sell the land or property subject to the leaseholder's interest being maintained.

PLANNING CLASSIFICATION

The developer when searching for 'green field' sites suitable for development, or for redevelopment sites, will be concerned to clarify the planning classification of the land and the possibility for change of use.

Land with outline planning consent

Outline planning application procedures provide both vendors and prospective purchasers with the opportunity to establish whether permission to develop land will be granted, without incurring the cost of preparing detailed plans. Outline planning approvals will be subject to conditions (reserved matters), for example, specification of the type of development, density, means of access, approval of detailed plans and design, including external appearance, siting and landscaping. The approval once obtained will expire within a period of three years, unless a detailed planning application is submitted to the local planning authority. The majority of parcels of land are usually sold with the benefit of outline, rather than detailed, planning approval.

Land with detailed planning consent

Land with the benefit of detailed planning approval will normally provide purchasers with the advantage of detailed plans for the development of a site. The permission may still be subject to conditions such as choice of materials, access, turning space for vehicles and lines of sight. Building regulation approval may also be required.

Development under a detailed planning approval must be commenced within a period of five years, beginning with the date on which the permission is granted or, where an earlier outline approval has been obtained, the date of that permission.

If work is not commenced within this five-year period, a fresh application with the associated risk of refusal will have to be made. Where a 'token' start is made on site, the local planning authority may serve a completion notice advising that the planning consent will be revoked if the development is not completed within a defined period of not less than one year.

Purchasers may find that although land has detailed planning approval it may not be economically viable to develop and local planning authorities may be reluctant to embrace alternative proposals.

Land included within a local plan or local area study

Such land may be zoned for immediate development or for development within a specified period of five or more years. The local plan may include land already developed and identify opportunities for redevelopment or change of use. Individual landowners are, however, under no pressure to sell and in fact may wish to retain land in its present use and, where a key site is concerned, may delay or prevent development of adjoining land. It is of course necessary for landowners or prospective purchasers to apply for planning approval in the usual way and such applications may be refused, particularly where the local planning authority is seeking to ensure comprehensive development of an area, of which the site in question forms only a part.

Land scheduled for future development will not receive planning approval until the due date, by which time the planning policy and local plan could be substantially amended.

Land zoned for development in a local plan, although without planning approval, may well change hands at substantially above the market price in its current use, in anticipation of development taking place.

Land with 'hope' value
Land just outside village or city boundaries may be viewed by speculators as having 'hope' value (hope that planning approval will ultimately be granted). Skilful assessment of the future potential of parcels of land likely to be released, under pressure, for development is common practice for many builders and speculators. Land in this category tends to sell at inflated prices, over the current use value, varying from a marginal surcharge, to perhaps 50% over the value of building land, depending on the degree of hope that the site will receive planning approval in due course.

Agricultural land
Land in this category with no apparent possibility of development will sell at agricultural value. The only possible scope for early development is in association with its agricultural use, for example living accommodation for farm workers or owner-occupiers. Such approvals are, however, subject to conditions. Long-term investment over 20 to 30 years is likely to prove advantageous to those companies with surplus cash who anticipate that development may be permitted in the long-term future.

FINDING LAND FOR DEVELOPMENT

The developer, in identifying land for residential development, may choose between an active and a passive role in locating and bringing land into the company's land bank. This choice will be subject to prevailing economic conditions which have a profound impact on the availability and viability of sites suitable for development.

In the early '70s viable land was difficult, if not impossible, to locate and many developers, in the scramble to acquire good land banks, paid prices which reflected demand and anticipated inflation, rather than the sale price of the completed dwellings. Developers were obliged to adopt a highly active role in locating land. By 1974, however, following the collapse in the property market, land was hawked from door to door by builders, estate agents, banks, speculators and private individuals. The '80s have seen a return to a more stable market, with demand and supply in a measure of equilibrium.

The developer will need to be involved in many site investigations, in order that one or two of his entrepreneurial endeavours come to fruition.

PASSIVE METHODS OF SITE FINDING

The landowner, estate agent or speculator may make a direct approach to the developer. For this to occur, developers should ensure that they have a good reputation for fair dealing and an established relationship with local and national estate agents. While such contacts can be invaluable in difficult market conditions with the ensuing scarcity of land, it may prove difficult to actually find suitable sites.

Advertisement

Land may be advertised in the local or national press or in trade journals by estate agents, solicitors, land-owners, banks or executors. Developers would do well to scan as wide a selection of these publications as possible. Often the advertisement will only provide the briefest of details, including approximate location, acreage and the method of disposal. The developer is then left to make a response to the advertisement and approach the vendor or his agent for more information. Once land has been advertised it may be subject to much interest, and in buoyant market conditions severe competition may develop, whichever method of sale has been adopted.

Estate agent

The estate agent may be consulted by the vendor at an early stage and either he or an architect instructed to apply for any necessary planning approval, prior to putting the land on to the market.

The agent, when instructed to sell land 'or property, will almost certainly appraise the development or redevelopment potential and advise his client accordingly.

The estate agent will retain a register of all builders and developers interested in land purchase, with full details of their requirements. When land becomes available the agent will circulate the details of the site, including acreage, planning condition and possibly a photograph, together with the method of sale – auction, tender, offers or private treaty. The circulation may on occasion be restricted to certain defined and known developers who are most likely to re-instruct the agent for the sale of the projected development. The agent's first objective is to obtain the best possible price for his client and secondly, if possible, to generate the opportunity to market the completed units. In normal or difficult market conditions, the agent is probably able to serve his client well by such introductions and contacts, particularly where the site will be sold by private treaty at a fixed price or by offers over a minimum sale figure.

In good market conditions, however, auction or tender will be more likely to provide the best price for the client, but because the land has been widely advertised the purchaser will be under no moral or other obligation to re-instruct the agent.

When the market is depressed, the agent may himself, via his own contacts, prospect for land suitable for development and become involved in site assembly. Agents may also act for purchasers in making investigations and enquiries.

From the above comments, it becomes apparent that the developer would be well advised to make regular contacts with estate agents in his own area or in areas where he wishes to extend his operations. These visits should be at not less than three-monthly intervals, ensuring that the correct particulars are maintained on the agents' files. Some agents automatically strike enquirers off the file if regular contact is not maintained. Most agents circularise prospective purchasers at regular intervals, to check on their continued interest. Failure to respond will result in deletion from their register.

Land speculator

The land speculator operates in two different ways, either using entrepreneurial initiative, negotiating time and ability but relatively little capital; or by investing on a long-term basis with the ultimate possibility of substantial capital growth.

In the first case the speculator with entrepreneurial initiative may identify land with numerous problems hindering development, and attempt to resolve these by negotiation. Frequently, development is only possible following land assembly, and agreements or options with numerous owners have to be negotiated before a viable site can be created.

Where site assembly is involved, the speculator fulfils a valuable function. Problems and bad feeling may arise, however, when the difference between the price paid per acre to the landowner and by the developer for the overall site exceeds a reasonable level, or individual land sales have been agreed by the speculator at widely different price levels, without apparent reason. This is particularly the case where the speculator 'sells on' options for each separate parcel of land forming the site and the developer is left to enter into formal contracts and legal completion for the purchase of the land in the usual way.

Equally, the speculator may identify a site without planning approval, enter into an option agreement with the vendor, and sell on the option once planning has been obtained. The mark-up should be fair and reasonable, the speculator being reimbursed for both time and enterprise. Occasionally when unsuspecting, perhaps elderly, landowners have signed option agreements without legal or professional advice, and the resulting mark-up by the speculator is excessive, the developer may feel tainted by the procedures involved.

Once the speculator has assembled and identified the land, he is often not over-anxious to draw attention to his activities and will therefore attempt to dispose of the site direct to the builder or developer without advertising or using an estate agent.

In the second case the land speculator with capital may acquire land with hope value land which may control or prevent development of adjoining land such as sight lines or access points, and key parcels of land which may ultimately form part of a larger site. The speculator's sole intention is to secure a profit without providing any input, even if this is not achieved for many years. Builders and developers themselves may also speculate in land in this way.

Bank or receiver

Land may be offered for sale when a builder has gone into liquidation. Such land will usually be channelled through an estate agent. Where personal contacts exist, sites may be offered directly to the developer by the bank or receiver (often a chartered accountant). It would be wise to fully investigate why such sites are on the market.

Private individual

A private individual who is a landowner may contact a developer direct without consulting any outside agencies. The developer may, of course, be only one of many approached.

Local authority

Local authorities, particularly where there is a policy of selling off land previously compulsorily acquired (for example, for housing and schools), often form a useful source of land for the developer. Sites are usually widely advertised and tenders invited, either directly through the local authority or via an estate agent, sometimes involving 'design competition'. Frequently the local authority will expect some form of planning gain using a planning agreement made under section 52 of the Town and Country Planning Act 1971. The developer is then legally bound to abide by conditions in the planning permission, which may well include, for example, building roads, schools, community centres, or providing parks and other open spaces.

ACTIVE METHODS OF SITE FINDING

The majority of developers are unlikely to adopt the passive role of waiting to be advised or only investigating advertised sites. The developer may follow a number of different avenues in his pursuit for suitable land. The greater number of developers are not necessarily confined to any particular geographical area and will, therefore, not only investigate the market potential in the immediate locality of their home base, but will be equally prepared to operate at a distance. The true entrepreneur will also investigate the potential of a locality while on business trips or holidays. This can be particularly profitable as a fresh look from an outsider may reveal untapped sales potential and markets not recognised by the local estate agent.

Market research is one key factor when assessing the potential of an area and this will be considered later in the chapter.

When actively searching for probable sites, the developer should pursue a variety of methods, including the following.

Planning lists

Any individual is at liberty to visit the offices of the local planning authority and ask to see the monthly or bi-monthly list of planning applications that have been submitted. It is also possible to monitor their progress through the planning process. Where such sites are owned by private individuals (not by another builder or developer) a personal approach, together with a good offer, may pre-empt the instruction of an estate agent or advertisement by the vendor to sell the site. An early approach to the vendor may also give the developer opportunity to assist in the planning process, possibly overcoming obstacles to the proposed development.

Where the application has been submitted by an estate agent or other agent acting on behalf of the vendor, a direct approach at this early stage may give the developer 'the edge' (a slight advantage in any later sale or disposal arrangements).

There are specialist commercial organisations who will, in exchange for an annual subscription, provide a service listing all planning applications and decisions made by the majority of local planning authorities. Subscribers indicate the areas in which they are interested and the relevant lists are sent each month. Such lists are also used by contractors to indicate possible opportunities for submission of tenders. Once a developer's attention has been drawn to a site, even though the planning approval may have been rejected, it may be possible to resolve the objections raised by the local planning authority. Often applications are rejected because more comprehensive development proposals are required, including land not in the vendor's ownership. In such cases the developer may be able to assemble a site including both the original and adjoining land to achieve a scheme that will be acceptable to the local planning authority.

Close study of applications and their results, including objections, enable the developer to build up a comprehensive survey of the current attitudes of the local planning authority to development proposals, and those sites likely to receive favourable consideration.

Structure plans, local plans and local area studies
In recent years planning authorities have gradually achieved their objective of adopting a 'positive' approach to planning (although developers may find this hard to believe), and structure plans, local plans and local area studies exist for many regions, towns and villages.

Close study of local plans and local area studies, together with a physical inspection of a locality, can reveal sites with potential for redevelopment, change of use, or green field sites. It is also possible to identify land scheduled for development in future years, particularly where the development of an area is delayed due to problems with infrastructure, for example where the release of land is delayed pending improvements to sewers or sewerage disposal facilities.

Development plans show future road improvements which may affect development, for example where new access onto an existing road is not permissible. By reading between the lines and closely studying local plans, it is sometimes possible to identify the probable expansion or pressure points on defined village or town boundaries, thus identifying land with hope value. Due to demographic changes, such as falling population, land can be released for residential development which was previously designated for other uses, such as schools and recreation grounds. The owners of such land may be unaware that circumstances have changed and the developer may have the edge in being able to acquire the site. Close study of local plans will invariably produce some results and often sites, although small, have scope for replacing one dwelling with several. However, owners are under no compulsion to sell and although land may be identified for development, it may in fact remain undeveloped for many years.

Personal investigation
This is the method with the greatest potential, but does involve time, perseverance, expertise and hard work. Having initially defined the area of interest, the developer can, with the aid of Ordnance Survey maps and on-the-spot investigations, identify sites with development possibilities. These may include infill sites or sites with low density development, which are suitable for redevelopment. The identity and addresses of landowners can be established by talking to local people. Contact with landowners may be made by post or by personal visits. Owners of properties with large gardens often have no idea of the development potential and value of their land. A reasonable offer may well be accepted, particularly where the area of the whole property is less than one acre, owner-occupied, and therefore exempt from tax. It should be emphasised that if the reputation of the developer for fair dealing is to be maintained, offers made for land found in this manner should be fair and reasonable, as from time to time speculators have acquired sites at far below their true value, in a similar way to door-to-door antique pedlars.

Once an area is known it is also possible that, where houses with large gardens and potential for demolition and redevelopment are offered for sale, the developer may be able to effect a purchase. The property may be resold with a reduced garden area and planning approval obtained for redevelopment of the remainder.

Personal investigation of areas will also undoubtedly lead to the possibility of land assembly from a variety of individual landowners, to form a viable and cohesive site. This may be in the form of land between existing dwellings or often the assembly and foreshortening of long back gardens in order to permit development. Before the 1947 Town and Country Planning Act, ribbon development was common along existing road patterns and land was left at the rear for agriculture, market gardens or allotments. It may prove necessary to purchase and demolish existing dwellings to provide suitable access. When site assembly is contemplated, options or conditional contracts will be essential.

Aerial photography

Perhaps the most sophisticated approach to land finding is the use of the helicopter or light plane and aerial photography. The combination of Ordnance Survey maps and aerial photographs is particularly useful in identifying undeveloped back land where ribbon development has taken place. Access to such sites is often obscure, possibly only by a footpath which may not be noticed at ground level. Aerial photography can also be utilised as a backup to the latest Ordnance Survey maps, to plot changes in boundaries and new development.

GENERAL PRINCIPLES

Locating land suitable for development requires tact, perseverance and a skilful expertise, linked with the experience to know when to 'push on' or 'pull out'! When expending time and money on negotiations or investigations, some vendors attempt to use the developer's expertise free of charge to obtain a valuation and appraisal of the development potential of their site, even to the extent of the developer obtaining the necessary planning approval and resolving technical problems. Some form of contract is, therefore, essential.

When dealing with landowners it is best to be known to be always fair, with offers close to market value, or an explanation made when this is not possible. Such a reputation tends to reap its own rewards, particularly from those vendors who do not care to sell via an estate agent.

The developer, whether obtaining land from a passive or active approach, will be committed to undertake an extensive and detailed market research appraisal and investigation of the site before proceeding to purchase.

METHODS OF DISPOSAL OF BUILDING LAND

The developer introduced to or locating land suitable for development will often have no control over the method of disposal. The vendor or his agent may already have decided to sell the land by auction, tender or highest offer. When the developer is actively seeking land, it may be possible to conclude the negotiations by private treaty, to obtain an option or to enter into a conditional contract. The alternative disposal arrangements have advantages and disadvantages for both vendor and purchaser, which will be revealed as each is examined in detail.

AUCTION

The cost to the vendor of selling land by auction is normally higher than by tender or private treaty – approximately £1000 above the standard percentage fee. When the market is buoyant, it will normally be in the vendor's interest to sell at auction. The site will usually be widely advertised locally, although a particularly valuable or large site will be advertised nationally. From the developer's viewpoint, competition may be fierce and the likelihood of acquiring sites by this method is not great. It is necessary for prospective purchasers to undertake detailed market research and a site investigation, and to prepare a feasibility study in order to identify the highest value that may safely be put on the site. It is essential to read the small print on the auction particulars, especially where obligations are being passed to the purchasers. It is common to include as the purchaser's responsibility such items as fencing, new roadworks, removal and reconstruction of septic tanks, connection of existing properties to new drains, and construction of garages.

In the auction room discretion must be used in bidding and the developer must have a clearly defined policy if the price exceeds the value calculated: he should either withdraw or bid only a marginal percentage above the calculated value. One danger is that prospective purchasers get carried away and on occasion acquire land on impulse without fully investigating factors which may influence the financial success of the proposed development.

Land sold at auction may have a reserve price and the site will only be sold when bidding reaches the reserve, the auctioneer advising at that point that the site is 'in the market'. It can be disconcerting at auction if the vendor or agents acting on the vendor's behalf bid up the price from the floor in the early or even later stages of the auction. The author recalls one occasion where the land was bought in three or four bids after his company's last bid. The agent subsequently contacted us to advise that the company's was the highest bid and asked if we would be prepared to proceed at that figure.

The successful purchaser at the conclusion of the auction is required to sign the auction particulars and pay 10% deposit of the purchase price. In effect this stage is equivalent to exchange of contracts in a sale by private treaty, with completion four weeks later. There is, therefore, no opportunity to withdraw or delay the transaction.

The auction particulars must of course be both detailed and accurate, as they form part of the contract for sale, and are usually in the form of a glossy brochure. One particular problem for prospective purchasers is that they are obliged, prior to the auction, to undertake a full and complete site investigation, including searches through a solicitor, at their own expense. The vendor is of course obliged to prove his title to the land in the normal way.

TENDER

The vendor or his agent may request that tenders are submitted for a parcel of land; the estate agent will give wide publicity to the site and circularise prospective purchasers. The tenders should be totally confidential and a closing time and date stated. It is preferable if the tenders are opened publicly with the tenderers given the opportunity of being present, so that fair play can be clearly seen to have taken place. In any event all participants should be notified of the result. It sometimes happens that, after tenders have been submitted, tenderers are advised of the highest figures and either are asked to submit, or themselves insist on submitting, an even higher one. This cannot be regarded as good practice.

It can be argued that tendering will give the best result from the vendor's point of view, as each purchaser is likely to submit his best offer and therefore in the absence of knowledge of the level of other tenders, may pay a figure far in excess of the nearest competitor. At auction the purchaser may have been able to acquire the site at a marginal figure above the next highest bid.

The cost of selling by tender can be fractionally greater than by private treaty (perhaps involving a glossy brochure) as it may be necessary to advertise the site more widely. Provided there is sufficient interest, tenders should also result in certainty of sale within a defined period.

Sometimes when land is offered for sale by private treaty and there is keen interest from several prospective purchasers, tenders are introduced to resolve the competition.

On occasion one hears of unusual circumstances surrounding tenders, where neither the vendor nor tenderers are present to affirm that everything was above-board. It may be possible, due to restricted publicity and advertising, for few tenders to be submitted and personal friends or acquaintances of the agent to be able to submit a low offer, or arrange for an offer to be submitted once all the tenders have been opened. This is of course unethical.

The author recalls that tenders were invited for a site for 40 bungalows in the West Country, overlooking the sea and a fishing village. The site was only advertised locally and my company only heard of the proposed sale via the foreman of a site in the same vicinity. Our land buyer approached the agent, who advised that tenders were expected in the region of £50 000. Extensive market research revealed that the site was substantially undervalued and a more realistic figure would be well over £100 000. A second visit to the agent produced the same guidance of £50 000. In the event a successful tender was submitted at £54 000, on the basis that all other enquiries were being similarly guided, and in fact tenders ranged from £50 000 to £52 500.

In normal circumstances, however, tenders are to the advantage of vendors and are the least satisfactory method of purchase from the purchaser's point of view.

PRIVATE TREATY
The vendor may offer the site for sale himself or instruct an estate agent to act on his behalf in the disposal of his property or land. The agent, having prepared particulars, will advertise and cirularise potential purchasers, but the sale price may be presented in the following ways.

Fixed price
A fixed price for the land is set marginally above market value. The agent will then use his best endeavours to sell at this fixed price, in the meantime advising his client of any offers received.

Open to offers
The agent merely states that offers should be made for the site, without providing the purchasers with any guidance regarding price. Once the agent has received a number of offers, it may well happen that each party is advised of the offers on the table and asked if they are willing to increase their offer. The process continues until all but one of the parties involved has withdrawn. This is a delicate negotiation and if at a later stage the prospective purchaser who made the highest offer withdraws, the other parties may have lost interest or not wish to participate.

Offers over a guide price
This is perhaps the most common format, where prospective purchasers are asked to make offers over a guide price, minimum sale price or are advised of a range of prices within which an offer may be acceptable.

Whichever of the above methods is adopted, once the vendor and purchaser have agreed on a sale price, the respective solicitors will be instructed to proceed with the preparation of draft contracts. The transaction should be subject to contract and the two parties are not legally bound until both have signed contracts setting out the terms of the sale and these contracts have been physically exchanged. Each party will then hold the contract signed by the other. The monetary consideration involved at exchange of contracts is usually 10% of the selling price.

Until contracts are exchanged, the parties are buying and selling 'subject to contract' and either party may withdraw from the transaction. Conversations or agreements may however leave the parties morally if not legally bound. In any event, from time to time vendors may receive and accept a higher offer for land after solicitors have been instructed, but before contracts are exchanged. This is much more likely to arise where the vendor must be seen to obtain the best possible price for the land, such as a trust, bank or other institution. Vendors may also, against the advice of their agents, enter into a contract race, where the first purchaser to sign the contract secures the land. This is particularly likely to arise when the original purchaser is taking an inordinate length of time to proceed.

COMPETITION

Local authorities or government departments, when disposing of important sites in inner cities or sensitive planning areas, may invite tenders for the site on the basis of a 'design competition' conforming to a planning brief. This will involve the developer in a substantial amount of design work, including both site layout and individual house designs. The local authority often requires some kind of planning gain in the form of roads, schools, community centres, to benefit the community at large.

In deciding which tenders to accept the local authority will be influenced by the design, layout and general presentation of the scheme; the assessment as to genuine architectural merit may be subjective. The local authority will not be bound to accept the highest, or in fact any tender.

The writer is aware of one scheme where the planning brief was ignored by a developer, who as a result achieved an increase in density and was able to submit a substantially higher tender figure than other developers who had conformed to the planning brief. In this case the highest tender was accepted, without other tenderers being given the opportunity to submit another offer on the basis of similar amendments to the original brief.

METHODS OF PURCHASE OF BUILDING LAND

Consideration has been given to the methods of disposal of land open to a vendor. Where, however, the initial approach to the vendor has been made by the purchaser, a slightly different situation may exist. The two parties may agree a price for the land or ask an agent to act on their behalf. Once the price has been agreed solicitors will be instructed and the legal process, which should be subject to contract, will proceed in the normal way. It is unlikely that other offers will be submitted, as the sale of the site will not have received publicity. The negotiating parties will however be free to withdraw from the transaction prior to exchange of contracts. Where the developer will be involved in a substantial commitment of time and resources in obtaining planning approval or resolving development problems, it is likely that the parties will enter into an option agreement or conditional contract.

OPTION AGREEMENT

An 'option to purchase' is a device used by many developers to secure building land during the planning and problem-solving period. In essence the developer pays a sum of money to the landowner in exchange for the landowner agreeing to sell the land at an agreed price, within a defined period. The advantage to the developer is that he is under no obligation to exercise the option and proceed with the purchase, whereas the landowner must sell the land to the developer if the terms of the option are met. Typically a landowner is offered a consideration of, say, £2000 per acre to grant an option to purchase, which may be exercised within 12 months by the developer. The developer is then free to resolve problems with services or infrastructure, obtain planning approval and if necessary negotiate similar options with owners of adjoining land in order to assemble a site. The developer could sell the option to a third party, or in fact exercise the option and proceed with the purchase even though all the problems have not been solved. The period of the option could also be extended with the agreement of the vendor in exchange for an additional payment. Some options can be long term with the vendor receiving substantial payments, perhaps equivalent to the value of the land in its current use.

The option is clearly to the advantage of the developer, in that:

- there is low initial capital commitment
- there is opportunity to resolve problems and obtain planning approval

- he faces less competition than would be found if the land was sold at auction or tender
- if the scheme is abandoned the option need not be exercised

On the other hand problems can arise where there is a substantial downturn in the market and it is not viable to proceed at the price agreed in the option agreement.

The landowner has the advantage of receiving a cash sum while still enjoying the possession of his land, but generally he does not have the security of knowing that the transaction will proceed. In the meantime he can only sell his land subject to the conditions of the option agreement.

CONDITIONAL CONTRACT

A conditional contract is similar to a normal contract to sell, except that the contract is subject to the fulfilment of certain conditions, such as planning approval being obtained, acquisition of sight lines or easements for drainage. In effect the developer is prepared to proceed with the purchase provided the site can be developed. The developer will be obliged to use his best endeavours to resolve outstanding problems and the vendor himself may independently attempt to meet the conditions imposed by the contract, if the developer fails to proceed with due diligence.

The conditional contract does give the developer the incentive to invest time and money in a project, with the background assurance that this investment will not be wasted. This method of procedure is less advantageous to the developer but provides the vendor with more protection of his interests.

SITE INVESTIGATION AND MARKET RESEARCH

Once a potential site has been identified, irrespective of how the site has been located or the method of disposal, it is essential that a detailed site investigation and market research is undertaken. This is necessary not only to establish the viability of the proposed development, but also to identify any restrictions or lack of availability of infrastructure.

In practice this investigation would normally take place before an offer was made and certainly before exchange of contracts. Following legal completion many aspects of the exercise would be repeated at the detailed design stage or when finalising sale prices.

Most companies will adopt a positive approach to site investigations and use standard forms or check-lists to ensure that no stone is left unturned in investigating every aspect of the site. In view of the substantial sums of money involved, risks must be reduced to the absolute minimum. Each aspect of this investigation will now be considered in detail.

PLANNING

The classification of land from a planning point of view was discussed earlier in this chapter, but the developer will need to establish not only that the site has a valid planning consent which has not expired, but also the conditions associated with the approval. Some conditions influence density and layout, while others merely affect design and the subsequent cost of house construction, including choice of materials such as bricks and tiles. Equally, other conditions under section 52 of the Town and Country Planning Act 1971 are negotiated between the planning authority and the applicant for approval and are classified as planning gains. In this case the local authority seeks to transfer a proportion of the appreciation in the value of the land as a result of planning approval being granted to the benefit of the community at large. The planning gains or conditions may take many forms, including:

(a) Dedication of part of the site as open space or parkland.
(b) Contribution to costs of infrastructure and services, or construction of such facilities, whether for the benefit of the site, or adjoining land and existing properties.
(c) Provision of leisure facilities and shops.

A point could be reached where the cost of meeting such conditions may result in the development of the site being delayed or abandoned.

It is important to contact the planning authority, in order to discuss the planning history of the site with the appropriate planning officer. The planning officer's attitude to proposals to develop a site can be assessed when only outline approval has been obtained or substantial modification is required to the detailed approval. Some planning authorities are helpful, while others are positively obstructive, and personal contacts and the cultivation of a good relationship with planning authorities are therefore essential. Once a developer is known as being 'sensitive' to the environment, with care and feel for both design and layout, the planning officer responsible for an area will tend to be more helpful and responsive.

In contrast, those developers whose prime objective is building houses at maximum profit and with minimum care for the environment, may experience difficulty.

Checks should also be made to establish that change of use of the land is not required and that there are no listed buildings or tree preservation orders affecting the site. Developers, before any planning application is made, sometimes create bad relationships with the local planning authority by clearing sites, ignoring tree preservation orders and demolishing listed buildings. Relationships once broken in this way may take a long time to heal.

Planning delays are legion and it is essential to know the track record and attitudes of the planning office responsible for the area in which the site is situated. The author has experienced such extremes as the time lapse from date of submission to receipt of detailed planning approval varying from five days to 18 months. The cost of planning delays with current levels of interest can rapidly erode profit margins.

BUILDING REGULATIONS

The building regulations do not impose the same degree of restriction on the developer as the planning authority; nevertheless, their implications in the development of proposed sites must be taken into account when investigating viability. The majority of the building regulations have little or no impact on the financial potential of a site, with one or two notable exceptions.

Cesspools and septic tanks

When mains drainage or a private drainage scheme is not available, drainage to each individual property will need to be either to a cesspool or a septic tank. Both require desludging from time to time, which is normally by pumping out using a tanker. The maximum effective length for pumping is 30 metres and the regulations therefore require that the cesspool or septic tank should be sited within this distance of a vehicular access. Any emptying should not involve the contents being taken through a dwelling place or place of work other than an open covered space. It is also necessary to obtain approval from the water authority to discharge the effluent of a septic tank, by means of land drains into the ground. The length of the land drains is governed by the absorption capacity of the ground. The water authority will reject applications for the use of septic tanks when absorption tests are unsatisfactory or where the siting of the tank could result in pollution to a spring, stream or well used for drinking purposes. The use of septic tanks or cesspools may have a significant impact on maximum permissible density of dwellings per hectare.

If approval for septic tanks cannot be obtained, the only alternative will be sealed cesspools of a capacity not less than 4000 gallons. These cesspools will require emptying at approximately six-week intervals. The cost per annum, which will be borne by the purchaser of the completed property, may well exceed £500 – which may affect sale prices and hence the land value.

Foundations

The foundations of a building will vary in design and cost depending on the bearing capacity and nature of the sub-soil. Both the building control department of the local authority and the National House-Building Council have become meticulous over foundation design, particularly since the drought of 1976, when substantial claims for subsidence were made. At that time many buildings, even those built 30 or 40 years ago, suffered subsidence damage, particularly on clay sub-soils. Where trees such as large poplars exist on the site, they absorb copious amounts of moisture from the soil, which may affect the water table locally. When trees are cut down, some sub-soils re-absorb moisture and expand, causing heave and structural damage to property. It is considered that after large trees are felled it may take up to 12 months for the sub-soil to achieve stability.

Where trees are to be retained on site, or are outside the site boundary and therefore cannot be removed in order to avoid possible subsidence in clay or similar sub-soils, part of the site may be sterilised (designated 'unusable') in order to keep buildings at a safe distance. The building control officer will usually give advice in this area and careful layout and design can usually maximise site usage.

It is useful to obtain permission to execute trial holes at various locations on the site to establish the nature of the sub-soil, bearing capacity of the ground, and the water table. One trial hole may prove inadequate, as ground conditions often change dramatically between one part of the site and another. There are specialist firms who will provide this service. The result of these tests will determine, for example, depth of foundations or need for special design such as raft construction or piles, problems associated with high water table for both foundations and drainage, need for de-watering, sulphate content of the soil and need to use sulphate-resistant cement.

The building control officer will often be aware of local ground conditions and at the early stage of site investigation his advice will be invaluable in determining probable additional costs.

Distance from boundaries

The building regulations require that walls to buildings should be so constructed as to prevent fire reaching the boundary and, as a consequence, possibly endangering adjoining property. The degree of fire protection needed is reduced as the distance from the boundary increases until no protection is needed (i.e. external walls may consist entirely of unprotected area). Generally speaking, walls within 1 metre of the relevant boundary should be entirely protected, except for small openings.

Fire precautions

The plans for high-rise buildings and buildings for public use, when submitted for building control approval, will also be scrutinised by the fire prevention officer of the local fire brigade. Requirements will include access for equipment and fire escapes, which may well affect layout of the site and space around buildings.

ACCESS TO THE SITE

Access to the site is an important part of the site investigations. Planning approval is often granted subject to satisfactory access being provided and it is therefore essential to approach the highways department of the local authority to establish both the *status quo* and the effects and requirements of any proposed development. Problems are sometimes difficult to spot and are certainly unlikely to be highlighted by the vendor or his solicitor. It will be useful to discuss some of the more common problems.

Ransom strips

'Ransom strips' arise in a number of situations where land for development can only be reached by crossing land not in the vendor's or developer's ownership. Perhaps the most common situation is where planning approval has been granted for development of land adjoining an existing earlier development. Access to the adjoining land may well have been provided by means of a road or 'hammerhead' and the road will almost certainly have been adopted by the local authority. The access road, however, may not actually reach the boundary of the site and the original developer may have retained a strip as narrow as 1 m. The purchaser will, therefore, need to acquire this strip before the site can be developed, or find an alternative access. Ransom strips are so called because they change hands at high values, often up to one third of the total site value. It could of course be argued that the original developer is entitled to some remuneration for the cost involved in constructing the original road and associated services. The alternative situation is that the owner of the adjoining land may be forced to sell the site to the original developer at a price well below normal market value, but above the price of any competitor who would have to buy the ransom strip as well as the proposed site.

Planning authorities have become aware of these practices and often now include conditions that roads are taken to the boundary of adjoining land, where future development is anticipated. The developer, however, may be able to circumvent this situation by making no provision for access roads within the layout, but leaving plots adjoining possible future building land undeveloped in anticipation of change in planning policy.

Access to classified roads

When access is required onto a classified road, approval must be obtained from the Department of Transport or local authority acting as their agent. Frequently no further or new access will be allowed onto classified roads until bypasses or other road improvements have been completed. Land scheduled for development may remain undeveloped for many years, pending solutions to traffic problems.

Sight lines

The planning and highway authorities will require sight lines at the junction of estate roads with other roads. Where the road is curved away from the junction on both sides, very long and wide sight lines will be required. Within the zone of space contained within the sight line, no construction or vegetable growth will be permitted over 500 mm high. Problems arise where the sight lines required cannot be achieved within the curtilage of land owned by either the vendor or proposed purchaser, and run onto adjoining land. It will then be necessary to negotiate with the adjoining owner, either to acquire the land in question or to obtain an easement to conform to the conditions in perpetuity. The position will, therefore, be very similar to that described for ransom strips in that the adjoining owner may demand a high price for the land in question or even refuse to sell. In the final analysis the only solution will be to find alternative access, or buy the whole of the adjoining property, if it comes onto the market.

Road widths and lengths

Local authorities usually produce design guides for roads within their administrative areas, laying down minimum standards of width, widths of footpaths and radius of bends, depending on the design, speed and type of road. Equally, if the access road is a cul-de-sac the design guide may provide for a maximum permissible length of up to, say, 300 m or a limit on the number of dwellings using the road. There is usually a maximum number of dwellings permitted off a private drive on new estates.

The local authority may insist that existing access roads are improved and widened before allowing development to proceed. When local authorities do not own the necessary land, and frontages of adjoining property are involved whose owners refuse to sell, the developer may be willing to pay, but be unable to achieve the desired improvements.

Private roads

The access to a site or any part of the site may be over a private or unadopted road. Such roads may or may not be subject to a public right of way or rights of way to specific landowners. Some local authorities may refuse to accept development of the site unless the section of the access road that is private has been adopted by the local authority. Although the local authority has powers to adopt private roads, it may be reluctant to apply them as the cost of the road construction will fall on the landowners proportionate to their road frontage. If, however, all the relevant landowners with road frontage request adoption the local authority are obliged to do so.

It is, therefore, essential that the developer obtains the necessary easement or rights of way from the respective owners, when access roads are to remain unadopted.

The usual procedure for roads within the curtilage of the development site is that they are dedicated to the local authority and adopted. The local authority therefore lays down the specification for the road construction and in view of the long-term maintenance obligations, insists on high standards of workmanship and materials. These high standards in rural areas, with kerbs, footpaths and parking bays, can result not only in high cost, but in aesthetic problems. On high quality developments, therefore, it is sometimes advantageous to leave the roads in private ownership to provide a rural feel, with grass verges rather than kerbs. A maintenance agreement with the owners of the site or a management company will be necessary.

Adoption of roads

Where the local authority is to be required to adopt the roads, the developer will be given the alternative of either:

(a) Depositing with the local authority a cash deposit covering the full estimated cost of the work. The deposit will be returned once the roads have been completed to the satisfaction of the local authority and adopted; or

(b) Entering into a section 38 agreement which will entail obtaining a road guarantee bond from a bank or insurance company. Unfortunately many smaller developers find such bonds difficult to obtain, since so many development companies failed in the property crash following the economic problems of the early 70s.

If a section 38 agreement is not available, in due course the house purchaser's solicitors are likely to hold a retention from the sale proceeds, pending adoption of the roads by the local authority.

PHYSICAL PROBLEMS AND CONSTRAINTS

When the land buyer is investigating a potential site, it is essential to walk over every part of the land. Site dimensions and levels should be checked, as dimensions on legal documents are often obscure or non-existent or classed as for identification purposes only.

Some aspects of the nature of the site have already been discussed when looking at the effect of the building regulations. Certain other physical problems and constraints will now be identified.

Shape of the site

Perhaps the most obvious physical constraint is the shape of the site and its effect on layout and density. In its simplest concept a site would have an optimum width of, say, 70 metres, comprising a 6-metre road, two 2-metre footpaths and plot on either side of 30 metres. If the site is too narrow, development may only be possible on one side of an access road and equally, where the site is marginally wider than 70 metres, the backland will be undeveloped and therefore relatively uneconomic. Each site must of course be judged on its merits and with skilful layout used to its best advantage.

The site may only be viable if adjoining land is included and in fact the planning authority may insist that only a comprehensive planning application will be considered. It may prove either impossible or too costly to acquire the adjoining land and the proposed scheme will therefore have to be aborted.

Contours

The contours of a site are obviously important and may add or detract from its development potential. Level sites are generally more economic to develop although deep sewers may be required and care with layout must be exercised to give interest and variety. Sloping sites, on the other hand, tend to offer more potential to the architect in both layout and design, but will invariably involve increased foundation cost and possibly pumps and rising mains to overcome drainage problems.

Steeply sloping sites may be totally or partially unsuitable for development and the writer can recall a site where only two thirds of the land was developable and the remainder barely suitable for inclusion in the gardens of the completed dwellings.

Present and previous use of land

It is important to trace the history of a site as far as possible, and identify its present and previous uses. A useful step is to inspect old Ordnance Survey maps, and the 6-inch 1906 survey will be found useful.

If the original and present contours are studied it is possible to identify suspect areas, where filling may have occurred. Trial holes may also disclose made-up ground but odd pockets may be difficult to identify. Often whole sites have been filled which will inevitably result in expensive foundation design.

Previous land use for industry in particular should be studied, as the soil may be contaminated with noxious substances, such as lead and asbestos. Previous development may also have left old foundations, concrete slabs and basements which must be identified and quantified for additional cost.

The most common problem encountered, however, is subsidence, either in areas of mineral extraction or, more often, when buildings are constructed on made-up ground. Circumstances can arise which are difficult to anticipate; for example, one site with which the author was involved was situated over a mile from the sea, but part of the site was on ground made up from Elizabethan times and included a harbour wall. The nature of the problem was only identified by studying early maps showing the mediaeval town and harbour at the Archivist Department of the local authority.

Flooding

It is often difficult to establish if a site is liable to flooding and it can be easily overlooked during the site investigation. A quiet river on a summer's day may be a raging torrent in February. The local authority or water authority will be aware of sites which are subject to flooding at regular intervals, such as low-lying land in river valleys.

Some knowledge of the geography of an area is important. A chalk stream, for example, may flow at a virtually constant level summer and winter, while flash floods may occur miles from a water course or in hollows well above the water table.

The most useful sources of information are the oldest local inhabitants who are usually aware of the circumstances regarding flooding in their area. On one site the author recalls contacting the oldest locals, who advised that a site had only flooded once in living memory and they were only too pleased to point out a 'flood line' still just visible on a number of buildings in the area after 30 years.

EXISTING SERVICES

Overhead electricity and telephone lines, although clearly visible and therefore easily assessed for their effect on a proposed development, may be overlooked. The public utilities concerned will advise on the possibility and cost of diversion.

Underground services are more difficult to locate and identify – the claim of the British Gas advertisement on television that 'you would not believe our main crossed here' is only too true. Easements for both gas and water mains may restrict development for a 4- to 10- metre swathe through a site, depending on the size and pressure of mains, and both are very expensive or impossible to divert. (Incidentally, if such mains are broken during the progress of the work, the developer will rapidly be aware of the necessity for an easement restricting development to within the stated distance.)

The presence of mains services and their location will generally arise from the solicitors' enquiries and searches, but their significance on layout can be underestimated. It is important to contact the relevant authority if the site is subject to an option agreement and solicitors therefore not instructed.

When making enquiries with the public utilities regarding availability of services it is essential to identify the position of existing services affecting the site. Often services are redundant but still live and in a different position to where they are shown. Test holes to identify the location of all existing mains and services are useful in the design of the proposed layout.

It should be noted that although gas or electricity mains pass across or near the site, this may have no relevance to availability of the respective services.

In conclusion, therefore, it is essential to investigate thoroughly the exact location of all mains services affecting the site and to assess the financial implications on layout and density or the cost of removal or diversion.

OWNERSHIP, LOCATION AND CONDITION OF SITE BOUNDARIES

The position of boundaries can be very important when fences or markers have deteriorated or been removed. It may be difficult to identify a precise boundary and it is essential that they are defined not only legally but practically on site in the presence, and with the agreement, of adjoining owners. Where boundary fences are in poor condition, the estimated cost of rectification should be assessed as part of the financial appraisal.

Existing 'defined' boundaries sometimes need monitoring: the author on one occasion was involved with a site where development was delayed pending completion of a sewerage scheme and one boundary advanced a few feet a year, flower beds, lawn and all.

TREES AND VEGETATION

The effect of trees on foundation design was discussed earlier but a physical inspection of the site should include the location of all major trees, particularly where they are required to be retained under a tree preservation order and may therefore affect layout and density.

MARKET RESEARCH AND AESTHETIC CONSIDERATIONS

GENERAL SITE APPRECIATION

When assessing the value of a site it is essential to walk over it and get a feel for the market potential. The majority of factors relating to site inspection will consist of legal, practical or factual matters, but we are now considering the aesthetics of the site.

The developer will use all the senses – seeing, hearing and smelling – when assessing the environment. The solar aspect may be important in determining the layout both of individual units and the whole development. Trees and contours all add to a sylvan setting and any attractive existing features may well be incorporated in a proposed scheme with advantage.

It is useful to photograph the site from a variety of angles, obtaining views both into and out of the proposed development; photographs often reveal factors overlooked at an initial inspection.

NATURE OF SURROUNDING ENVIRONMENT

The nature of the environment surrounding the site is of obvious importance, including possible future uses of the land. In a rural situation proximity to motorways, pig farms, sewage disposal works and unsightly light industrial operations such as scrap or builders' yards, have a significant impact on site value. In the built environment the exact nature of surrounding development is equally important, including the relative market level, proportion of private or local authority housing and its density, and whether high- or low-rise. The level of vandalism and dereliction should also be noted. In addition it may be necessary to investigate the nature of any industrial development, and the direction of the prevailing wind, to verify that the site will not be affected by effluent, smoke, fumes or smell. This may be necessary even if the industry is situated many miles from the site.

Some adverse factors can be mitigated by mature tree planting, fencing or other screening and careful layout and design.

ACCESS TO SITE

The nature of the access road to the site and adjoining development can be influential with regard to market potential. If the access to an up-market development is via a local authority housing estate or area lacking in amenities it may prove more difficult to sell the completed units.

Conversely, if the access passes through high quality housing to a less ostentatious scheme, sales will be positively aided.

PREVAILING WIND AND RAINFALL

Although of little importance in most parts of the United Kingdom, prevailing wind and rainfall may be a very important consideration when developing exposed sites, near the coast or in the Highlands of Scotland and the Western Isles. Wind speeds are accelerated in valleys and building in exposed locations can invite structural damage both during and after construction. Dwellings should be designed and constructed to higher standards, particularly with regard to water penetration. The author can recall one development on the West Coast of Scotland, where tiles were stripped from the roofs several times a year, in spite of each time being nailed and clipped.

Local rainfall variations in hilly areas can also be significant and potential sites should be selected with care after discussion with local people or local weather experts.

NOISE

Nuisance caused by noise, whether from roads, railways, aircraft or adjoining owners, must form part of the investigation. Each source may vary with weather conditions or time of day, week, month or year. Aircraft, for example, may use different flight paths depending on wind direction and road noise tends to be more noticeable in certain weather conditions. If in doubt, the developer should check the levels of noise at different times and make enquiries with local people.

Double glazing, although increasing cost, can be very effective in reducing noise levels.

LEGAL RESTRICTIONS

The solicitor acting on behalf of the purchaser will have the opportunity to examine the conditions prior to exchange of contracts. Any legal restrictions that may have been imposed by the vendor or already have been included in earlier conveyances of the land or property can be identified. Before signing the contract the purchaser should in any event read the document carefully and arrive at a full and clear understanding of any restrictions imposed.

The legal restrictions which affect the value and development potential of land can broadly be included under the headings of restrictive covenants, rights of way, and easements.

Where land is bought at auction it is essential that the purchaser or his solicitor undertakes the necessary searches and reads carefully the smallprint in the brochure.

RESTRICTIVE COVENANTS

Restrictive convenants are the most common legal restriction imposed on the purchaser and often go back over many years. Where the vendor has a continued interest in adjoining land, each time any part of the land is sold, he may impose virtually any condition which is acceptable to the purchaser. These conditions may not only be for the vendor's own benefit, but for his 'successors in title'. The most common restrictive covenants are as follows.

Limited density

Land is sold subject to only one property, or a defined number of properties, being built on the site. This restriction will apply irrespective of the view expressed by the planning authorities.

Designs to be approved

The vendor reserves the right to approve the designs of the proposed buildings. This restrictive covenant is often included in village or rural sites and can result in lengthy delays and extreme frustration. One site with which the author was involved was delayed for two years, with constant revision to the proposed design.

Furthermore, the vendor's views on the design may conflict with the planning authority and meeting the requirements of both can be fraught with difficulty. The addition of the term in the contract 'such approval not to be unreasonably withheld', or time stipulations on approval, may assist the purchaser.

Houses of a certain value, size or type

Where the vendor was attempting to define quality, a common restriction included in conveyances earlier in this century was that houses must cost not less than, say, £1000. With the relatively low levels of inflation in that period, such conditions may well have sufficed, but would be a short-term and unrealistic method of quality definition in these days. Such a restriction on land coming onto the market is irrelevant, but nostalgic.

Currently, to define quality, the floor area or number of bedrooms may be stipulated; a restriction may also be imposed on the proportion of detached, semi-detached or terraced dwellings.

Boundaries

Where a vendor wishes to protect his own interests, those of his 'successor in title' or of an adjoining owner, a restriction may be imposed that no development will be permitted within a defined distance of a certain boundary or existing dwelling.

No overlooking

Proposed dwellings on the land will not be permitted to incorporate windows at either first floor level or both ground and first floor levels, facing in a certain direction or overlooking adjoining property.

Height

The number of storeys or height of buildings may be restricted, for example by defining the maximum height of the ridge above ground level.

Restrictions on the use of land or dwellings

Certain restrictions are often imposed for the common good of inhabitants in an area. For example, development must comprise private dwelling houses only, with no trade or business (other than perhaps a doctor or dentist), no caravans or boats to be stored, no dogs, pigs or poultry, no sheds or sheds over a certain height, no loft conversions or extensions.

The author has encountered a covenant on a site bounding the River Test in Hampshire, where from the back of the house to the boundary no construction of any sort was permitted above ground level and trees and vegetation could not exceed 6 feet in height.

The above and similar restrictions will of course affect both the value of the land and its viability for residential development.

Restrictions can be removed by consent from the original vendor or 'his successors in title'. Applications can also be made to the Land Tribunal to modify or discharge the restrictive covenant, but this will of course take time.

POSITIVE COVENANTS

Covenants may be included in the contract and conveyance imposing an obligation on the purchaser, which has both cost and value implications. Examples would include the provision and maintenance of fences, roads, drains, sewers and private sewage disposal works. The site may of course benefit from such covenants which have previously been imposed on adjoining landowners.

Easements

An easement is a right to use another person's land in some way. The most common easements affecting sites are rights of way, restrictions imposed by public utilities for passage of gas, water, electricity and telephones, rights of support, discharge of water and rights of light. The site may, of course, benefit from easements imposed on adjoining land.

An easement can come into existence by express grant or by contract, but it can also arise in at least three other ways.

At common law, it can arise if the right has been exercised from 'time immemorial'. In this context, 'time immemorial' means from the year 1189. However, it is not necessary for the user to prove conclusively that the right has been exercised back to this date. If he can prove that it has been exercised for 20 years before the date of an action, it will be presumed that it has existed from 'time immemorial'.

In addition to that, the common law will presume that there is a 'lost modern grant' if the right has been exercised for 20 years.

Finally, the Prescription Act 1832, still in force, provides that easements other than rights to light become absolute if enjoyed for 20 years. Where the right has been enjoyed for 40 years, it is to be considered 'absolute and indefeasible'. In the case of easements of light, the right is 'absolute and indefeasible' after 20 years.

Public rights of way

Public rights of way of any width are classified as highways. The term 'highway' includes roads, carriage ways, cartways, horseways, bridleways, footpaths, causeways and pavements.

The Rights of Way Act 1932 provides that where a way over land had been actually enjoyed by the public as of right and without interruption for a full period of 20 years, the way shall be deemed to have been dedicated as a highway, unless there is sufficient evidence that there was no intention during the 20-year period to dedicate it.

When considering the development potential of land incorporating bridleways or footpaths and the cost associated with overcoming the problems, there are two alternative options: either to incorporate the footpath within the layout of the development, or to apply to the local authority for the footpath to be diverted. The procedure to be followed will usually involve the parish council and the placement of public advertisements in order that any objections or representations can be made. This procedure will take upwards of six months to complete and may result in costs, if a potential scheme is delayed.

Private rights of way
Private rights of way apply to an individual or group of individuals and not to the public at large. Care must be taken to establish the facts surrounding the right of way, especially where the use appears to have lapsed, but the right of way still exists. Rights of way may be extinguished like any other easement, by negotiation and formal deed between the respective parties, probably in exchange for monetary considerations. Alternatively, it is possible to mitigate against any loss by arranging insurance cover.

Rights of way are often played down by vendors and appear dormant but once negotiations have been legally completed, or work commences on site, are vigorously enforced by the beneficiary. Mistakes can be costly and the author recalls one scheme where the beneficiary of a right of way waited until a house purchaser was due to move in before exercising his rights, thus deliberately causing the maximum disruption to the developer.

Easements for services
Public utilities have a statutory right to be granted easements to cross land, and although such easements are usually obtained by negotiation, where landowners object, the courts will ultimately override any objections. In rural locations, where development may not have been envisaged, such utilities may cross sites in unfavourable positions, severely restricting the layout.

Easements for large water mains and high pressure gas mains will restrict the use of the land within a defined distance of up to 3 metres from the main. Building, tree planting or change of ground levels will be totally forbidden. Deep main sewers can similarly 'sterilise' land as many local authority engineers draw 45-degree lines from the sewer to the underside of foundations to determine minimum distance of buildings.

The cost of diverting mains services and public utilities can be very expensive and in certain situations virtually impossible.

Rights of support, water and light

Where adjoining owners enjoy benefits from the indirect use of land such as 'right of support' or 'right of light', the developer may be obliged to ensure that such rights are maintained both during the development period and in perpetuity. Such rights will obviously affect the use of a site and the layout of development upon it.

Insurance

Where restrictive covenants and rights of way appear to have lapsed and extensive investigations fail to locate any individual able to enforce or enjoy the benefit from such rights, it is possible to take out indemnity insurance against the remote possibility that anyone emerges with the legal right to enforce the covenant or right of way. The insurance policy must cover the total cost of any possible claim, plus an allowance for inflation. Premiums are usually reasonable, provided the investigation is thorough and well documented and supported by affidavits.

VACANT POSSESSION

The vendor may have agreed to sell land with vacant possession, but at the date set for completion be unable or unwilling to provide it. Agricultural land, for example, may be subject to a tenancy agreement or grass keep. Vacant possession will be delayed and will prove costly, if not virtually impossible, to obtain.

In the built environment property may be squatted or sub-let. To obtain an eviction order through the courts could mean a lengthy legal process, possibly entailing adverse publicity.

SERVICES

Availability of mains services is a key part of the site investigation. If any mains services are not available, even though the proposed development has planning approval, it may prove impossible to develop the site. It is not enough to visit or telephone the offices of the local authority, water authority and public utilities, to verify the availability of services. It is essential to obtain confirmation in writing not only that services are available on or adjacent to the site, but in addition that they are adequate in capacity, and the cost of connection.

FOUL SEWER

The water authority now have the responsibility for foul sewers, but they often delegate certain aspects of administration and maintenance to the engineer and surveyor's department of the local authority. Inspection of the water authority sewer maps will reveal sizes of the mains, manhole positions and the relevant invert depth and cover level. The relationship between the sewer or sewers and the site should be examined and checked to ensure that access to the sewer is possible without requiring easements from adjoining owners. If easements are required, the identity of the adjoining owner and the difficulties likely to be encountered should be verified.

The presence of a sewer does not necessarily imply that connection is possible. The size of the sewer may be of insufficient capacity to take the additional effluent from the proposed development, or the capacity of the sewage works itself may be insufficient to cope. Many developments have been delayed for years pending completion of new or improvements to existing sewage works.

Where invert levels are not suitable for the site to be drained by gravity, the additional cost of a rising main and pumps will need to be quantified. Excessively deep sewers in bad ground conditions or below the water table must also be taken into account.

An essential factor to establish is whether the sewer is public or private. Local authorities do not automatically adopt sewers and when development has taken place, sewers have to be specifically dedicated by the developer. Where the sewers are private an easement will be required from the original developer to effect a connection. There is normally no problem in arranging connection to a public sewer, subject to capacity.

If main foul drainage is not available and a private sewage disposal scheme is to be included with the development, permission will be required to discharge any effluent into water courses or underground strata. If the sewage disposal works is to be situated off-site, a suitable site must be located and purchased and easements obtained from any owners whose land the sewer crosses. Septic tanks and cesspools were discussed earlier under 'building regulations'. Where main drainage is not available additional costs are certain to arise.

SURFACE WATER SEWERS

The previous observations regarding foul sewers apply equally to surface water sewers, except that the water authority has no statutory power to obtain easements for storm water sewers.

In many cases soakaways are used as an alternative to storm water sewers. Approval is required from the water authority to use soakaways and before acceptance it may be necessary to prove by absorption tests that ground conditions are satisfactory.

Soakaways to the roads and houses of a development will usually be cheaper than surface water sewers. Where the water authority refuses permission for their use the onus is on the developer to secure a satisfactory outfall for a sewer to a ditch, stream or river, and obtain the necessary easements. Often the outfall will be off-site and it may be necessary to provide a storm water sewer of over a mile to achieve an outfall acceptable to the water authority. The actual design and construction of the outfall will also necessitate approval by the water authority in order to ensure that erosion does not occur.

The cost of provision of such sewers and the associated easements can be very high and therefore affect site value.

ELECTRICITY

Electricity is usually available, except in extremely remote areas. The electricity board should always be contacted, however, to confirm the availability of the supply and the cost of connection, to establish whether a substation will be required and any delays expected in meeting the project programme. If the substation is located within the curtilage of the site, it will be necessary for the developer to dedicate the land to the board.

Connection charges are often mitigated if electric cookers, immersion heaters, or electric central heating are installed in the proposed dwellings on the development.

GAS

Gas is a desirable but not essential service. British Gas should be contacted to check if a service is available on or adjacent to the site, and the cost to the developer of provision of any new or extension to existing mains. The developer will normally bear the full cost of the supply.

WATER

The water authority must be contacted to establish if a mains water supply is available and that it is of an adequate size and pressure to serve the development. The water authority has statutory rights to obtain easements to run water mains across adjoining property, but obviously if adjoining owners object delays may arise.

Water mains are expensive and the water authority will charge the full cost of any extension to the developer. It is possible to enter into a guaranteed revenue agreement with the water authority whereby the income from the water charge over a 12-year period is offset against the capital cost and the developer is only liable for any shortfall on an annual basis.

If the individual service to a property (not mains) will need to cross the land of an adjoining owner, an easement will be required.

If mains water is not available, permission will be required from the water authority to extract water from a well or borehole. The additional cost of the borehole pumps and storage tanks will of course be borne by the developer.

TELEPHONE

Overhead telephone services are free (to the developer). The charges for underground services, however, vary in different areas. The developer will normally be given the opportunity to tender for the excavation work and laying of ducts and cables in association with the development.

STREET LIGHTING

Negotiations will be necessary with the local authority, frequently at parish council level, regarding the provision of street lights. The capital cost involved will be borne by the developer.

MARKET RESEARCH

The appraisal of the actual site, including aesthetic considerations, has already been discussed. It is worth emphasising the necessity to walk or drive around an area to get the feel of a district. Visits should be made on more than one occasion and at different times of the day or week.

The final aspect of the site-finding exercise is to assess the market potential of the area and investigate those external factors which will affect sales and site desirability. It is also important to assess the general economic situation, including the cost and availability of finance, not only for the developer, but also ultimately for the individual house purchaser. The market research exercise may be carried out independently of the actual site investigation. Discussion with the local estate agents up to a 10- to 20-mile radius of the site, the local authority and local people, will be helpful as they are usually only too aware of the advantages and drawbacks of a locality. As many people as possible should be interviewed to obtain a cross-section of response and opinion to the questions outlined below.

EMPLOYMENT

Employment prospects in an area and the type of work available should be verified. Investigation should be made of the distance and ease of access including the estimated travelling times to all towns and cities within commuting distance. There may also be a possibility of a demand for retirement or starter homes.

PUBLIC TRANSPORT AND GENERAL AMENITIES

An accurate report should be made of all public transport facilities including ease of access to the nearest railway station, motorway or airport. The times and frequency of services of trains and buses should be included.

Ease of access to the beach or countryside may also be a factor ultimately affecting sales potential.

SHOPS, DOCTORS' SURGERIES AND OTHER LOCAL FACILITIES

The location of village shops, post office, churches, doctors' surgeries and the nearest town and hypermarkets should all be noted. With the wide availability of private transport their location may be of little signficance unless the primary demand is for retirement homes, when prospective purchasers will be heavily dependent on local services.

EDUCATION

The distance of the site from primary and secondary schools, and their reputations, may be a consideration. Where there is more than one secondary school the method of pupil selection or the identification of catchment areas may be all-important. In some localities market prices of residential property are directly linked to and affected by school catchment areas, where a school has a very good or very bad reputation.

SURVEY OF EXISTING DEVELOPMENT

It is also useful to undertake a survey of the existing stock of dwellings both overall and currently on the market, together with a detailed appraisal of the other developments in progress and their respective sale prices. Part of the skill of successful development is in identifying and satisfying gaps in the market which offer higher than usual returns.

FEASIBILITY STUDY

When the site investigation and market research have been completed, before making an offer to purchase the site it is essential to undertake a financial appraisal or feasibility study.

The structure of the development or construction company will affect the nature of the feasibility study, depending on whether the functions of funding, construction and marketing are all undertaken by one company or are subdivided between several different companies. Assuming that only one company is involved, the first step is to prepare a sketch layout and quantify the house types and prices of the proposed development, to provide a gross financial return.

Offset against this return will be all the various costs involved in the development, including:

- *Professional fees*
  Architects' fees
  Planning and building regulation fees
  National House-Building Council fees
- *Services*
  Foul and storm water sewers
  Electricity
  Gas
  Water
  Telephone and street lighting
- *Roads and footpaths*
- *House and construction costs*
  Types and floor area and price per square metre
- *Plot siteworks*
  Drainage
  Fences
  Drives and paths
  Landscaping

- *Marketing costs*
  Legal fees
  Agents' fees and advertising costs
- *Administration and overheads*
  General overheads
  Interest calculated from projected cash flow
- *Profit expected*

The above costs and profit deducted from the gross return will provide a residual valuation of the site.

As with all residual methods of valuation, any error in the calculation will be directly reflected in the land valuation, for example when the land value is 20% of gross return, a marginal error of 5% in cost will affect the land value by 25%. The residual valuation should of course be cross-checked against a valuation made on the comparative basis before any offer is made.

The cost associated with any of the problems discussed above, including the costs of any delay, should be incorporated in the feasibility study.

CONCLUSION

Site finding is a skilful and difficult undertaking, fraught with pitfalls and blind alleys. The landbuyer should intuitively distinguish those opportunities worth pursuing from those where time and resources will be expended to no effect. Theory is no substitute for practical experience and this experience is often only bought at a high price.

This chapter should form a basis of a comprehensive check-list for successful site investigation, but is certainly not exhaustive. The developer should prepare a standard site investigation and market research format, which leads the landbuyer through a series of comprehensive procedures. This site-finding format should be continually updated as new problems are encountered.

8 Valuation of Trading and Land Stock

INTRODUCTION

It will be apparent from even a cursory glance at the preceding chapter that with relative ease, and often with no lack of management application, an apparently valuable asset can rapidly revert to a financial liability. On the other hand, land stock of low initial cost may rise a hundredfold in value upon receipt of planning approval or solution of other problems restricting its development.

In the building industry land stock is perhaps more significant in the balance sheet of the majority of builders than trading stock. This is particularly the case where builders do not maintain a stores department or utilise a yard, and in fact many builders function only on the basis of direct delivery from the builders' merchant to the site. In such circumstances either credits are arranged with merchants for surplus materials less a restocking charge, or they are sold or scrapped. Nevertheless, some builders do maintain their own stores, particularly when the company is engaged in small works.

VALUATION OF TRADING STOCK

The valuation of trading stock will normally take place only once or twice a year to coincide with the date of the end of the builder's financial year or half-year, although larger companies may prepare quarterly accounts. This valuation will be undertaken by the storekeeper, assessed and verified by management and checked by the auditor.

If the 'prudence' concept is followed there should be a tendency to undervalue rather than overvalue stock in the building industry.

ACCOUNTING POLICY
The Statement of Standard Accounting Practice No. 9: Stocks and Work

in Progress (commonly known as SSAP9) was issued in May 1975, and revised in August 1980, by the Accounting Standards Committee of the Consultative Committee of Accountancy Bodies, CCAB Limited. This consists of:

The Institute of Chartered Accountants in England and Wales
The Institute of Chartered Accountants in Scotland
The Institute of Chartered Accountants in Ireland
The Chartered Association of Certified Accountants
The Institute of Cost and Management Accountants
The Chartered Institute of Public Finance and Accountancy

Although there is no legal requirement for companies to comply with SSAP9, auditors will expect the financial accounts of companies to meet the guidelines laid down. Failure to do so may well lead to the qualifying of the published accounts.

A revision is proposed to SSAP9, details of which are set out in 'Exposure Draft 40' (ED40) published in November 1986 (see Chapter 12).

In order to conform with SSAP9, companies must include a note in their accounts to the effect that:

'Stocks are valued at the lower of cost or net realisable value. Cost comprises materials, labour and production overheads and net realisable value is based on selling prices, less distribution costs.'

The relevant clauses of SSAP9 state that the determination of profit for an accounting year requires the matching of costs with related revenues. The cost of unsold or unconsumed stocks will have been incurred in the expectation of future revenue, and when this will not arise until a later year it is appropriate to carry forward this cost to be matched with the revenue when it arises. If there is no reasonable expectation of sufficient future revenue to cover the cost incurred (e.g. as a result of deterioration or obsolescence) the irrecoverable cost should be charged to revenue in the year under review. Thus stocks need to be stated at cost or, if lower, at net realisable value.

In order to match costs and revenue, cost of stock should comprise that expenditure which has been incurred in the normal course of business in bringing the product to its present location and condition. Such costs would include all related production overheads even though these may accrue on a time basis.

NATURE AND ORIGIN OF STOCK

It is necessary to identify the nature of typical building materials held in stock by a contractor or developer. These would normally comprise such materials as cement, sand, aggregate, bricks, blocks, concrete and steel lintels, timber, sheet materials (plasterboard, plywood, etc.), windows, doors, joinery, kitchen fittings, roofing and floor tiles, sanitary ware, plumber's fittings, structural steel work, glass, paint, drainage goods, etc.

It will be immediately obvious that:

(a) The majority of materials outlined above are bulky and therefore expensive to double-handle.
(b) Each material has a different rate of deterioration
(c) The most efficient delivery arrangement will be direct from the builders' merchant or manufacturer to an individual site, rather than to the builder's store.
(d) Materials used via a builder's store with subsequent double-handling may well result in additional costs of at least 25%.

When considering the on-cost on stocks the builder must take into account the employment costs of storekeepers, stock lost owing to obsolescence and deterioration, insurance, interest on capital invested, and overhead costs associated with administration and floor space.

The amount at which materials are charged out to sites on stores issue notes must therefore reflect the whole of this on-cost if the stores are to be operated on a profitable basis.

Storage costs often exceed the value of goods stored during the normal turnover period. In recent years, however, inflation in material cost may have overridden this factor.

Many builders do not consider it financially viable to maintain a stock of materials at a yard. However, where a company is involved in small works or renovation of existing buildings, it may be essential. Some builders, in order to assist with the viability of maintaining a yard stock and operating a store, actively encourage direct sales to the general public.

Stock may be acquired either as a stock order from a merchant or manufacturer or from surplus materials returned from site on the completion of a project.

VALUATION AT COST

SSAP9 states that it is frequently not practicable to relate expenditure to specific units of stocks. The ascertainment of the nearest approximation of cost gives rise to two problems:

(a) The selection of an appropriate method for relating costs to stocks (such as job costing, batch costing, process costing, standard costing).
(b) The selection of an appropriate method for calculating the related cost, where a number of identical items have been purchased or made at different times (such as unit costs, average cost or FIFO – first in first out: see below).

In selecting these methods, management must exercise judgement to ensure that the methods chosen provide the fairest practicable approximation to actual costs. Furthermore, where standard costs are used, they need to be reviewed frequently to ensure that they bear a reasonable relationship to actual costs obtaining during the period. Methods such as base stock and LIFO (last in first out) do not usually bear such a relationship.

The method of arriving at cost by applying the latest purchase price to the total number of units in stock is unacceptable in principle because it is not necessarily the same as actual cost and in times of rising prices, will result in the taking of a profit which has not been realised.

One method of arriving at cost in the absence of a satisfactory costing system is the use of selling price less an estimated profit margin. This is acceptable only if it can be demonstrated that the method gives a reasonable approximation of the actual cost.

Costing is discussed in detail in Chapter 9. Most builders use a simple cost system for job costing (specific order costing) and the stores department may well just be treated as another job or cost centre with monthly costing which is balanced and closed on an annual basis. Many builders are unlikely to develop sophisticated costing techniques for their stores department, which will usually only represent a small fraction of the total materials purchases for the business as a whole.

The most common methods of valuation in construction companies are:

- FIFO (first in first out) – the calculation of the cost of stocks on the basis that the quantities in hand represent the latest purchases or production.
- Replacement cost – the cost at which an identical asset could be purchased or manufactured.

VALUATION AT NET REALISABLE VALUE
SSAP9 states that net realisable value is the amount at which it is expected

that items of stock can be disposed of without creating either profit or loss in the year of sale, i.e. the estimated proceeds of sale less all further costs to completion and less all costs to be incurred in marketing, selling and distributing directly related to the items in question.

The comparison of cost and net realisable value needs to be made in respect of each item of stock separately. Where this is impracticable, groups or categories of stock items which are similar will need to be taken together. To compare the total realisable value of stocks with the total cost could result in an unacceptable setting off of foreseeable losses against unrealised profits.

The initial calculation of provisions to reduce stocks from cost to net realisable value may often be made by the use of formulae based on predetermined criteria. The formulae normally take account of the age, movements during the past, expected future movements and estimated scrap values of the stock as appropriate.

In reality, owing to the fact that the majority of stock retained by a builder may well be surplus materials returned from completed contracts, valuation on the basis of net realisable value will be the most frequent method adopted.

PHYSICAL DETERIORATION OF STOCK
Practically all building materials are affected by one or a combination of the following:

- extremes of temperature
- dampness
- method of stacking or storing
- accidental or wilful damage
- avoidable or unavoidable wastage

Sometimes deterioration may be difficult to detect and, perhaps even more important, actual realisable value may be negligible and in some cases negative, in that costs will be incurred in carting away.

OBSOLESCENCE OF STOCK
Obsolescence may result from:

- change of fashion (sanitary ware, windows etc.)
- change of size (metrication)
- introduction of new and cheaper substitutes (plastic)

EXCESS OF STOCK

When stocks are held which are unlikely to be sold within the turnover period normal to a company, the impending delay in realisation increases the risk that deterioration or obsolescence will occur before the stocks are sold. Such stocks should therefore be written down when assessing net realisable value.

VALUATION OF LAND STOCK

Land stock may represent a significant factor in the balance sheet of many building companies. Often land owned by the company for many years is shown at cost and few people, other than the directors and possibly the company's bank mangager, are aware of the true value of the land stock.

If the land was revalued and stated in the balance sheet at its current market price this would of course result in the company making a book profit. A tax liability would therefore arise but the cash may not be available to meet this obligation. Where, however, the company is making a loss, it may be possible to mitigate this loss by revaluing the company's land bank, without incurring any tax liability.

When a company's land bank is shown at cost and its true value is not reflected in share prices it may, of course, be ripe for a takeover bid.

ACCOUNTING POLICY

In order to conform with SSAP9, most companies include a note in their annual accounts to the effect that:

> 'The individual parcels of freehold land held for development are valued at the lower of cost or estimated net realisable value. Cost comprises the purchase consideration including professional fees and net realisable value is based on the anticipated net selling prices. Independent professional valuations for land held for development have not (or have) been obtained.'

Alternatively an even briefer statement is sometimes included, such as:

> 'Stocks and land, including development costs and construction thereon, are valued at the lower of cost and net realisable value.'

LAND BANKS

House building companies tend to use their land banks in different ways.

Some companies endeavour to maximise profits from the land element of potential development. This can be achieved by holding sites for long periods and delaying the start of actual work on site for periods of up to, say, five to ten years. (Planning approvals must of course be renewed every five years.) Other companies derive their profit primarily from the construction process with a shorter land bank cycle of, say, up to three years.

It must be appreciated that inflation in land and house prices tends to distort the profit earned on land and the development process. It is important to develop budgetary control techniques and costing records within the company to clearly identify where profit is being made on development. All too often the profit earned on an individual house or indeed a development as a whole is less than would have been made if the site had merely been left undeveloped and sold at the end of the development period.

ACCURACY OF VALUATION

There are two methods commonly used in the valuation of land – direct comparison of capital values, and the residual method.

Direct comparison of capital values

The value of land is estimated by comparison with the value of similar land in the locality, provided there is sufficient evidence from recent sales for the valuer to use as a base.

Residual method

A calculation is made of the estimated gross return from a development project less;

- construction costs, including siteworks, roads and sewers
- architect's fees
- planning and building regulation fees
- legal and estate agent's fees
- overheads and interest on capital invested
- profit required

The balance will equal the residual valuation of the land. When this residual method is employed it is obvious that any error made in any part of the estimate will be directly reflected in the residual valuation.

In practice professional valuers tend to prefer the comparative method and builders the residual method, but for valuations for annual financial or management accounts it would perhaps be prudent to take an average of the result obtained using both methods.

Whichever method is used, certain factors have to be taken into account by the valuer in reaching a decision as to a realistic estimate of site value, such as:

- *Economic factors*

State of national economy
Availability of finance for developer and purchaser
Interest rates
Supply and demand in locality (need for accurate market research)
Demographic changes
Local employment conditions
Proximity and availability of schools, shops, etc.

- *Legal factors*

Restrictive covenants
Existing easements
Easements required
Approval of scheme by third party
Vacant possession (squatters)
Sight lines
Ransom strips
Private and public sewers

- *Infrastructure and services*

Existing roads and access
Proximity and capacity of existing public sewers
Availability of gas, water and electricity supplies

- *Engineering problems*

Made-up ground, mining, bearing capacity of soil
Springs, streams/rivers, flooding, water table
Existing foundations and basements
Previous use of land (i.e. lead works, chemicals, asbestos, etc.)
Invert depths of sewers, pumping station
Septic tanks and cesspools, approval for discharge of effluent

- *Planning and environmental problems*

Classification of land, agricultural land, land with hope value, land
    scheduled for development (usually in development or local plan)
Outline planning approval, detailed planning approval

Built environment, redevelopment or change of use
Existing planning approval may not be viable
Planning conditions, open space, density, play areas, height and design of
  buildings
Character of area and immediate environment

CONCLUSION
Continual rises in land values cannot necessarily be viewed as an
automatic process. In fact it is possible, particularly on inner-city sites, for
land to have a negative value. Whichever method of valuation is used, any
of the problems outlined above may have a serious and dramatic effect on
the valuation of a potential building site.

When the comparative method of land valuation is used problems may
sometimes arise where unrealistic transactions are used as a guide or base
value, particularly at the point when land values are about to fall, as
happened in 1973.

When land is developed it is important in the management accounts to
clearly identify the source of profit – from land appreciation, construction, or marketing.

9 Costing

The construction industry is noted for its high rate of liquidations. Perhaps one of the most significant contributory factors is the failure of builders to maintain adequate written records of business transactions. Often the smaller the company the greater the propensity for this particular weakness to develop.

For efficient management of a company, records should be maintained in at least three categories:
- Financial accounts
- Cost accounts
- Management accounts

Each of these divisions of the accounts records are of course interrelated and will now be examined in detail.

FINANCIAL ACCOUNTS

All companies are obliged to produce a balance sheet and profit and loss account on an annual basis. These must be prepared in accordance with the provisions laid down in the various Companies Acts, particularly 1948, 1981 and 1985.

Although the accounts are drawn up for the benefit of the proprietors or shareholders of a business, the primary objective of such accounts could be said to establish the amount of tax due to the Inland Revenue.

The annual financial accounts of companies presented to shareholders must be filed with the Registrar of Companies. As public documents they can be scrutinised by anyone prepared to pay the search fee.

SMALLER COMPANIES
In the Companies Act 1981 an option was given for certain smaller

companies (provided they are not public companies) to produce modified or shortened accounts for filing with the Registrar of Companies. In order to be classified as small a company or group of companies must meet at least two out of the following three criteria:

(a) annual turnover not exceeding £1 400 000.
(b) balance sheet total not exceeding £700 000.
(c) average number of employees not exceeding 50.

If a company meets these requirements in any year and is therefore entitled to the accounting exemptions for that year it will also be entitled to the same exemptions for the following year, regardless of whether or not it meets the criteria.

A company qualifying to be classed as small is entitled to the following accounting exemptions:

(a) It need not file a profit and loss account.
(b) It need not file a director's report.
(c) It may file a modified balance sheet.
(d) Certain information normally required to be given in the notes of the accounts may be omitted.

In addition the notes to the accounts need not include the directors' emoluments. Modified accounts are not intended to give a fair and true view of the company and it is therefore not necessary for such accounts to comply with the disclosure provisions of SSAP.

This opportunity to file or publish modified accounts does not limit the requirement to prepare full accounts for the shareholders. The objective of a company taking advantage of these provisions, therefore, is to conceal as much of its activities as possible from the outside world and therefore maintain a degree of confidentiality.

A smaller building company may be asked to provide more detailed financial information than is contained in the modified company accounts when applying to join a list of approved contractors or applying for a tenancy of, say, a builder's yard or offices.

It should perhaps be mentioned that there are also accounting exemptions for medium-sized companies (annual turnover not exceeding £5 750 000) but these are modest and are barely worth the effort and expense of preparing separate accounts for the shareholders and filing with the Registrar of Companies.

One of the problems facing the very small builder is lack of time and accounting expertise. There can be a tendency for such firms to collect details of all cash or cheques received from clients on the one hand, and all cash or cheques paid out for labour, materials, plant or services on the other, and pass the entire batch to the accountant at half-yearly or yearly intervals. In such circumstances the only indication of the company's well-being (and possibly a poor one at that) will be the state of the bank balance, until the accountant has produced the accounts for the year.

Usually such very small building enterprises will be engaged on work of short duration and will therefore be less prone to encounter the problems associated with the valuation of work in progress discussed in Chapter 12. As a result the accounts produced will tend to reflect a fairly accurate view of the profitability of the business.

PREPARATION OF COMPANY ACCOUNTS

For the larger builder with an accounts department, or at least the assistance of a bookkeeper, all financial transactions will be recorded on a regular basis and in a systematic manner. The objective will be to identify the financial effect of each transaction on both the company and its creditors or debtors. To this end a double-entry system of book-keeping, where each debit has a corresponding credit entry, will be used, which provides an arithmetic check of the books.

Each year an annual report and accounts will be drawn up which contains three main elements:

(a) The profit and loss account. This account is credited with all the income earned by the company and debited with all the expenditure incurred. The balance of the profit and loss account represents the net profit or loss for the accounting period. In effect it shows the flow of money through the company for the trading period.

(b) The balance sheet. The balance sheet does not relate to a period but sets out the book values of the assets, liabilities and capital as at a particular point in time. The balance sheet is not intended to show the current monetary worth of the company at the date upon which it is prepared. For example, fixed assets are normally valued at cost, less provision for depreciation, and current assets at cost or net realisable value, whichever is the lower. The values at which many of the assets appear in the balance sheet, therefore, may be far removed from current market value.

(c) Sources and applications of funds account. This account shows how the company raises finance during the year and what the finance was used for. It shows the movements in the company's liabilities and assets during the trading period.

STRUCTURE AND CONTENT OF THE ACCOUNTS

There are three factors which influence the content and presentation of company accounts: the law, the accounting profession and certain other bodies.

The Companies Acts of 1948 to 1985 make certain requirements regarding the content and presentation of company accounts. The 1981 Act in particular lays down how the information is to be presented and provides two formats for the balance sheet and a choice of four formats for the profit and loss account. The Act also requires disclosure in connection with the balance sheet of movements in share capital, debentures, fixed assets, reserves, provisions for contingent liabilities, and capital commitments. On the profit and loss account, disclosure is required of turnover and pre-tax profits by type of business and significant geographical areas, interest payments, taxation, staff payments, depreciation, auditor's remuneration, income from listed investments and payments for the hire of plant and machinery.

Smaller companies are exempt from some of these disclosures, as already mentioned above.

The accounts also have to be prepared in line with the accepted practice within the accounting profession, as laid down in a series of Statements of Standard Accounting Practice (SSAPs) issued by the Accounting Standards Committtee.

A detailed assessment of the majority of the SSAPs is outside the scope of this book, except for SSAP2 which is discussed below and SSAP9 which is discussed in detail in Chapter 12.

The various SSAPs, with the exception possibly of SSAP16 which requires companies to produce current cost accounts, may be regarded as binding upon both the company's accountants and its auditors. If there is a serious departure from these laid down guidelines the auditor may refuse to accept that the accounts are a 'true and fair view' of the financial affairs of the company and accordingly qualify the accounts to that effect.

Other bodies impose rules regarding the presentation and content of accounts on member companies. The Stock Exchange, for example, requires that its members prepare their accounts in accordance with the SSAPs and that there is a geographical analysis of turnover and operational profit for activities outside the UK. In addition the place of operation of subsidiaries must be given and the particulars of associated companies together with the directors' interests in the companies' shares.

ACCOUNTING PRINCIPLES

SSAP2 laid down fundamental accounting concepts which were largely incorporated as a legal requirement for the first time in the Companies Act 1981. The Act specifies four fundamental accounting principles which must be applied:

• Going concern basis. The company shall be presumed to be carrying on its business as a going concern.
• Consistency. Accounting policies must be applied consistently from one financial year to the next. This is partly to ensure that any increase in profitability can be identified as the result of improved efficiency rather than a change in the method of compiling the accounts. Where accounting methods are changed this should be disclosed.
• Prudence. All items must be determined on a prudent basis and should err on the side of caution and in particular:
  (a) Revenue and profits must not be anticipated, but should be recognised by inclusion in the profit and loss account only when realised in the form of cash or of other assets, the ultimate realisation of which can be assessed with reasonable certainty.
  (b) All liabilities and losses which have arisen or are likely to arise in respect of the financial year to which the accounts relate or a previous financial year must be taken into account, including those which only become apparent between the balance sheet date and the date on which the balance sheet is signed.
• Accruals. All income and charges relating to the financial year covered by the accounts must be taken into account without regard to the date of receipt or payment. This is commonly referred to as the 'accruals' concept. In other words, revenue should be shown for the period in which it is earned and not when it is paid. This will ensure that revenue and cost have been more correctly matched. Consequently revenue is recognised as having been earned when sales are made and not when the debt is settled, and the balance sheet will therefore including details of pre-payments both made and received by the company.

The Companies Act 1981 also provided that in determining the aggregate amount of any item in a company's balance sheet or profit and loss account, the amount of each individual asset or liability included in that amount shall be determined separately. For example, in calculating the amount at which stocks are to be stated, the test 'lower of cost and net realisable value' should be applied to each individual material, rather than to the total stock-holding.

When the directors consider that it is essential for some reason to depart from these fundamental accounting principles a note must be included in the accounts stating the nature of the departure, the reason for it, and its effect.

COST ACCOUNTS

The financial accounts for a building company would not give any indication of the profit or loss on any individual project but only the financial position of the company as a whole. The majority of builders therefore prepare a second set of accounts known as the cost accounts.

Cost accounts are only prepared at the discretion of the directors of the company and are not a legal requirement. Many smaller builders are unable to allocate the financial resources or staff to provide cost accounts and, with the consequential lack of accurate costing information, run greater risks of insolvency.

The primary objectives in producing cost accounts are to provide:

(a) The detailed information to determine the profit or loss on individual projects or an aspect of the company's business transactions.
(b) An accurate assessment of project results to provide a backup and feedback to the estimating department for more precise tendering for future work.
(c) A check against target costs or standard costs and a long-stop for the budgetary control of individual projects.
(d) The basis for calculating cash flow on individual projects.

The cost accounts are concerned with the composition of cost and the source of profit. Although the financial accounts provide a basis for calculation of profit there is no concern with how or where the profit (or loss) arises. On the other hand the cost accounts are not concerned with debtors, creditors, assets, liabilities or personal accounts.

The financial accounting system was historically well established before the concept of cost accounts was introduced. A distinct division therefore developed between the two methods of accounting.

INDEPENDENT COST AND FINANCIAL ACCOUNTS

As will be seen later in this chapter, the type of analysis used for the financial accounts is unsuitable for the cost accounts. This means that the original data must be separately reprocessed for the cost accounts.

A control (or total) account of all costs arising for a defined period (day, week or month) can be reconciled with the postings to the individual cost records for each project to ensure that the figures are balanced. With this system, however, there is no direct link with the financial accounts unless there are corresponding control accounts within those accounts. When this is not the case there will almost certainly, however, be periodic attempts to reconcile the two sets of accounts, by comparing the profit shown in the financial accounts with that revealed in the cost accounts. Because the two sets of accounts are administered independently it is relatively easy for clerical errors to arise and for items to be omitted from the costs, particularly internal transfers such as stores, transport and plant charges.

Many smaller companies, through lack of expertise, staff or financial resources, will be obliged to adopt this system of independent cost and financial accounts. Obviously where frequent attempts are made at reconciliation the cost accounts may be reasonably accurate. Accuracy is of course particularly important when a builder is engaged in small works and uses the cost records to prepare the final account and sales invoice for the client.

INTEGRATED COST AND FINANCIAL ACCOUNTS

In order to ensure that the cost accounts are a proven and reliable record it is essential that the cost and financial accounts are integrated. To this end the normal procedure is to reconcile the two sets of accounts at the close of the accounting period (close down). The accounting period adopted by most companies in the construction industry is either the last working day of the calendar month or the last day of the calendar month. This coincides with the normal trading and credit arrangements of builders' merchants and suppliers. The cost accounts will therefore be closed down on the same date.

By the use of control accounts in both the financial and cost accounts it will be possible to ensure that both sets of accounts are balanced and integrated. A control account is merely an extra account inserted at the back of a ledger or kept separately to make the ledger self-balancing. Items are posted to the individual ledger accounts in the usual way but when the postings are complete the total is posted to the control account. At the end of the accounting period the balance of the control account will be equal to the sum of the balances in the ledger account, thus proving the ledger.

As all documentation processed through the financial accounts will therefore also be processed and costed to the cost accounts, the monthly reconciliation of the two will bring to light any clerical errors or omissions from the cost accounts. Unfortunately this only proves that the total costed each month to the various cost centres is correct, but does not overcome the problem of invoices or other documentation inadvertently being costed to the wrong project.

ANALYSIS OF COST

Cost is defined in SSAP9 as being:

'that expenditure which has been incurred in the normal course of business in bringing the product or service to its present location and condition. This expenditure should include, in addition to cost of purchase, such costs of conversion as are appropriate to that location and condition.

Cost of purchase comprises purchase price including import duties, transport and handling costs and any other directly attributable costs, less trade discounts, rebates and subsidies.

Cost of conversion comprises:

(a) Costs which are specifically attributable to units of production, i.e. direct labour, direct expenses and sub-contracted work.
(b) Production overheads.
(c) Other overheads, if any, attributable in the particular circumstances of the business, to bringing the product or service to its present location and condition.'

The costing for any individual contract or development project could be analysed as follows:

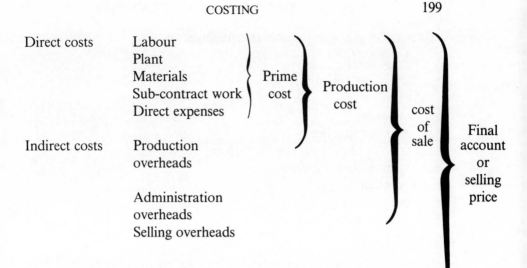

Direct costs   Labour
Plant
Materials   Prime   Production
Sub-contract work   cost   cost
Direct expenses

                                       cost
                                       of   Final
Indirect costs   Production   sale   account
overheads   or
                                               selling
Administration   price
overheads
Selling overheads

Profit or loss

In the building industry the normal practice is to cost net excluding the majority of overheads unless they are site-related. Most cost systems therefore concentrate on the prime cost. The costing of indirect costs or overheads is discussed in detail in Chapter 11.

SIMPLE HISTORICAL COST SYSTEM
It is normal practice in the building industry to cost all items gross. Any retention and cash discount, therefore, would be ignored in the cost accounts but dealt with separately in the financial accounts. Trade discount, however, would usually be deducted from the cost unless it was received as a rebate from the supplier when the company as a whole reached a certain level of purchases.

The simplest form of cost system merely amounts to an analysis or separate cost record for each individual contract or development project. No distinction will be made between the various elements of cost such as labour, plant and materials. The cost will simply be kept for each project as a running total entered by hand in a cost ledger. Indirect cost will be similarly costed to an analysed overhead account.

The production of a single cost figure per contract or even a very limited split of, say, labour, materials and expenses, is not particularly helpful to the surveying or management staff, although of course better than nothing. It is therefore normal practice to provide a more detailed cost breakdown under key cost headings arising on contracts or development.

Typical cost headings for contracts might be:

• Directly employed labour
• Labour-only sub-contractors
• Materials
• Own stores
• Nominated suppliers
• Labour and material sub-contractors
• Nominated sub-contractors
• Hired plant
• Own plant
• Own transport
• Special expenses

In the case of development projects administered and constructed by the builder a similar breakdown could be used. The cost headings for nominated sub-contractors and nominated suppliers, however, would be deleted as development projects would not normally be administered by an independent architect and therefore nominations would not arise.

Additional cost headings would, however, need to be included for:

• Land
• Legal fees
• Estate agent's fees

These basic breakdowns of cost do enable the surveyor or management to identify the total cost allocated to certain cost centres each month and with the aid of this basic information it is possible to produce a cost value reconciliation statement (see Chapter 11).

With such a limited cost breakdown, however, there is insufficient information to relate costs to work sections, other identifiable parts of an individual project or bill of quantity items. More detailed cost breakdowns are discussed later in this chapter.

CLOSE DOWN OF COSTS

Monthly close down of costs will usually occur at the end of each calendar month to coincide with the similar close down of the financial accounts. After the close down date most companies will allow a period of up to, say, 14 days for processing the various items of paperwork through both sets of accounts. This will include any late documentation from inside or outside the company. Depending on the efficiency of the staff of the accounts department the cost accounts for the previous month should be available to management within a maximum period of a further seven days, making a total maximum delay of 21 days. Where accounts have been computerised it may well be possible to accelerate this programme, as discussed later in this chapter.

DIRECT OR PRIME COST

In order to appreciate the reasons why cost records may be inaccurate at any given point in time and therefore will need adjustment before any cost value reconciliation can take place, it will be useful to examine the thinking behind a typical cost system. Obviously an individual company may deal with each cost centre on a different basis from the one discussed, thus varying the propensity for inaccuracies to occur.

Directly employed labour

Methods of remuneration of directly employed labour were discussed in detail in Chapter 6. Whichever method is adopted the wages clerk will be involved in checking time sheets and/or bonus calculations in order to calculate the wages due to operatives.

The time sheet filled in by the operative will need to provide certain basic information:

- The contract or project number, for easy identification of cost centres.
- Hours spent on each site during the day or part of a day if working on more than one site. This is particularly important for operatives working in small works departments of large companies or for small builders where frequent moves from one site to another occur.
- Where sophisticated cost systems have been introduced a division of the time sheet into hours spent on each operation or work section will be essential.
- An indication of the time spent on work which is not directly productive, such as working in the yard or stores, driving or travelling.

Management may need to provide encouragement and at worst assistance to operatives in the completion of time sheets.

There will of course be a delay between the completion of time sheets by the operatives, or bonus calculations by the bonus surveyor, and the actual payment of wages including any expenses and allowances. In the construction industry this delay for processing does not normally exceed two or three days, with a maximum of seven days (one week's wages in hand). Deductions from wages paid to operatives such as PAYE, national insurance, superannuation or court orders for maintenance will only be processed through the financial accounts. The on-costs on labour such as employers' national insurance contributions, CITB levy, holidays with pay scheme and other more indirect on-costs such as allowances for severance pay and legislation affecting employment, sick pay, allowance for employer's liability and third party insurance, will be processed through both the cost and financial accounts. As far as is possible it is preferable to charge the actual cost incurred rather than a percentage assessment to the cost accounts. This should ensure that any discrepancy between the cost and financial accounts each week that is charged to a variance account is very small, less than, say, £10 for the whole of a financial year.

On individual time sheets there may be hours of non-chargeable time, for example unproductive time spent waiting in the yard or time spent by apprentices in training or at college. Such costs will either be absorbed on a pro rata basis into the cost of existing projects or charged to the overhead accounts.

The cost of the payroll will usually be charged to cost accounts each week. At the end of the calendar month when the time sheet may apply to two accounting periods, the accountant will either:

(a) Allocate the total cost of the payroll to the calendar month in which the wages were paid.
(b) Allocate the total cost of the payroll to the calendar month in which the last day of the time sheet falls.
(c) Divide the cost of the payroll between the current month and the next month's costs, pro rata to the exact number of days worked in the respective months.

The majority of companies will opt for alternative (a) or (b) for ease of administration. This will result in directly employed labour being slightly undervalued from time to time.

Monthly salaries will obviously be costed on a calendar month basis and with the exception of site-based staff the majority of salaries will probably be costed to overheads.

Labour-only sub-contractors

Many companies use a certification system for the payment of labour-only sub-contractors (see Chapter 6) which makes the costing process relatively simple. The builder's surveyor will either check the information supplied by the sub-contractor or measure the work carried out during the payment period, usually weekly, but occasionally for longer periods of up to a month.

The monetary valuation of the measurements will form the basis of the payment each week. The certificate should indicate the name of the contract, contract number, name of sub-contractor, nature of work, the gross payment to date, previous payments and current payment for the period, together with details of deductions for such items as retention, insurance and CITB levy. The deductions will be controlled in the financial accounts and the gross payment for each period will be posted to the cost accounts.

For simplicity the amount to be costed is best highlighted in dark type or shown in a separate box on the form. The accountant is faced with the same problems regarding the correct allocation of cost to the current or following month for payment certificates near or straddling the month end, as was discussed under directly employed labour.

Payment certificates will usually need to be prepared in quadruple:

Top copy	to sub-contractor
Second copy	to financial accounts
Third copy	to cost accounts
Fourth copy	to surveyor's file

The builder's surveyor obviously occupies a key role in this process. Any inaccuracy in weekly measurements and subsequent payments to sub-contractors will be translated directly into both the financial and cost accounts. It may be weeks, months or even years before slaphappy surveying methods are identified by management. It must be emphasised, therefore, that it is essential that management monitor and frequently check the competence of their surveying staff, the methods of measurement used, and that sub-contractor's accounts are accurate and up to date. It is imperative that management allocate sufficient staff resources to achieve this objective.

Materials
The bulk of the documentation passing through the accounts and surveying departments will relate to materials purchases. The various stages of the purchasing process include enquiry, quotation, placement of order, delivery with delivery note, invoice received, invoice checked and

approved, and statement reconciled and account paid, as discussed in Chapter 5.

Although strictly speaking the company is responsible for the cost of materials immediately the order is placed, the normal procedure is for costing to be delayed until the invoice has been checked and approved for payment.

The author was once involved in the takeover of a small company where costing was undertaken manually in a large ledger. A cost entry was made when materials were ordered, and updated at delivery, when the invoice was received, checked and then paid; notes were made of any problems at each stage.

(A costing system for materials invoices is outlined later in this chapter.)

Own stores

Costing for own stores is a very similar process to that for materials invoices except that the priced stores issue note (see Chapter 5) will take the place of the materials invoice. Because the documentation is produced internally and no cash transfer is involved there may be a tendency for the pricing of stores issue notes to be deferred, with the consequential possibility of late or under-costing.

The stores department would of course be subject to complete financial control with all wages for storemen, overheads, transport and materials purchases being debited to the control account, and stores issue notes being credited. The resultant profit or loss on stores will form part of the financial accounts.

Nominated suppliers

The costing process for nominated suppliers also involves the client's quantity surveyor. At each interim valuation the builder will pass the original nominated invoices received during the month to the quantity surveyor for inclusion in the interim certificate and payment. A duplicate copy of the invoice will be retained by the builder's surveyor for record purposes.

JCT 80 provides that

'Full discharge by the Contractor in respect of payments for materials or goods supplied by the Nominated Supplier shall be effected within 30 days of the end of the month during which delivery is made less only a discount for cash of 5% if so paid.'

A problem may obviously arise for the builder where the nominated supplier makes deliveries late in the month and the relevant invoices are not available at the date of the valuation. Equally, the valuation may take place just prior to the end of the month and deliveries be made after the valuation but before the end of the month. In the first case the client's quantity surveyor may possibly include an estimate of the cost in the valuation but in the second case the amount will be omitted from the valuation completely. The builder, however, is committed to pay in accordance with the principles laid down in JCT 80, which may well cause cash flow problems.

The invoices may be processed through the cost accounts in the same way as that described below for materials invoices. More commonly, however, the builder's surveyor will certify payments on a similar basis to that described for labour-only sub-contractors.

If payments are to be certified the builder's surveyor may delay the issue of the documentation until the interim certificate for the main contract is received from the architect. In such circumstances the copy certificates for processing through the cost and financial accounts may not reach the accounts department until after the date of the monthly close down and may therefore be costed to the following month. Payment should of course be made on time.

The amount certified by the client's quantity surveyor may not necessarily be identical to that certified by the builder's surveyor due to such factors as replacement of any damaged supplies, claims or contra-charges. Discrepancies must be accounted for during the cost value reconciliation procedure (see Chapter 11).

Labour and material sub-contractors

The procedure for payment of labour and material sub-contractors will usually follow that described for labour-only sub-contractors and interim payments will be supported by a certificate issued by the builder's surveyor. The sub-contractor will normally make a request for interim payment and raise a tax invoice for VAT purposes on completion of the work.

In order to avoid disputes and unnecessary duplication of effort, where work requires remeasurement this will take place at a joint meeting of the builder's surveyor and the sub-contractor.

Measurement and subsequent payment for work executed may take place at weekly, monthly, or at random intervals and therefore may not be related to the date of the main contract valuation or the builder's costing periods. It would be usual practice to ensure that the payment is costed to the month in which the work is carried out. However, where the payment relates to work executed in two costing periods the accountant may choose the last period, the period when the majority of the work was undertaken, or split the payment between two cost periods. In practice the simplest solution will normally be followed in that the cost will be allocated to the same period as the payment in the financial accounts. The important point to consider is that the builder's surveyor must be fully aware of company policy when adjusting the cost for cost value reconciliation purposes.

The invoices will of course be retained on the surveyor's file and the internal certificate will form the documentation for both the financial and the cost accounts. The certificate, besides containing the basic information outlined previously for labour-only payments, may also give an indication of the amount of the sub-contract and target cost.

Nominated sub-contractors

Under JCT 80, sub-contract NSC/4 or 4a, the payment procedure for nominated sub-contractors is essentially controlled by the client's quantity surveyor and the date of issue of the valuation certificate. The payment request or invoices from the nominated sub-contractor will be received and checked by the builder and passed to the client's quantity surveyor at the time of the interim valuation. The client's quantity surveyor, and if necessary the relevant consultant, will also check the invoices or payment requests and include the agreed amount for each nominated sub-contractor in the interim certificate. The amount certified for any individual sub-contractor may of course be less than that claimed. The builder must pay the nominated sub-contractor the amount certified within 17 days of the date of issue of the interim certificate. The builder's surveyor will be unable to certify payments to the various nominated sub-contractors until after the interim certificate has been received from the architect.

It is probable, therefore, that the internal payment certificate will not be raised in time for inclusion in the current month's costing as they will be received by the accountant after the close down date for the month. The builder's surveyor will therefore need to make the necessary adjustments for cost value reconciliation purposes.

The payment will be costed gross and any retention or cash discount will be accounted for in the financial accounts. When contra-charges or claims have arisen between the builder and the nominated sub-contractor for such items as damage, breakages or delays then obviously the amount certified by the builder will vary from that certified in the interim certificate.

In order to distinguish between the internal payment certificates for labour-only sub-contractors, labour and material sub-contractors, nominated suppliers and nominated sub-contractors, it may be useful to use different coloured documentation for easier identification.

Hired plant, special expenses, legal and estate agent's fees

Invoices for hired plant, etc., will be processed through the cost and financial accounts in the same manner as for materials invoices detailed below. Hired plant invoices may create a slight problem where the hire period extends across two accounting periods. The accountant will need to make the policy decision as to which accounting period the invoices should be costed in, or whether the cost should be split.

Own plant and transport

Cost documentation for the company's own plant and transport will be produced internally by the plant and/or transport department. There may be a tendency either to overlook plant charges or to delay the issue of the costing documentation.

The company, as a policy, will need to establish whether small tools and minor items of plant are charged to the project at cost and credited on their return to the plant department, or whether all items of plant, including small tools, are to be charged on a similar basis to that used by plant and tool hire companies. It may be prudent to offer contract management a discount of, say, 10% off normal plant hire charges for the company's own plant to encourage its maximum use.

The plant department will probably have a number of direct employees, including drivers, fitters and administrative staff, and it is therefore essential that proper accounts, with correct proportions of overheads, are maintained to establish the department's profitability.

COSTING SYSTEM

The cost system now outlined could apply not only to materials invoices but also to invoices for hired plant, special expenses, overheads, legal and estate agent's fees, and in part to certified payments and the company payroll.

Orders

Separate orders should be used for each project. If materials for different contracts are included on the same order this may well lead to the supplier repeating the presentation on the invoice, thus necessitating a split before costing.

The supplier should be requested:

(a) To supply two copies of invoices.
(b) To provide a separate invoice (in duplicate) for each purchase order.
(c) To include the project number and the name of the site on the invoice.

Blanket orders

May apply to more than one contract, but 'call off' orders should be for specific projects.

Invoices received

If the supplier does not provide a duplicate invoice a photostat copy must be made. One invoice should be stamped 'original' and the other 'copy'. The copy invoice should be retained by the accounts department and the original sent to the buying department or other department or individual responsible for checking the invoice (see Chapter 5). Once the invoice has been checked and approved and returned to the accounts department the original invoice will be processed through the financial accounts and the copy invoice through the cost accounts. If invoices remain unchecked after the 14th of the month they will be excluded from the monthly close down of the cost accounts, treated as late invoices and costed to the following month.

Procedure within the financial accounts

Approved invoices can simply be placed on a file, 'unpaid invoices for the month of ...' and filed alphabetically and in date order under the name of the individual supplier. The relevant invoices for each supplier can, at the appropriate time, be reconciled with the statement and the supplier's account paid. Where invoices recorded on the statement have not been received or have been mislaid, copies will be required from the supplier. Equally, incorrect invoices may need to be adjusted by means of a credit note issued by the supplier or a debit note raised by the builder.

Many larger companies adopt the procedure of raising a debit note for any errors on invoices. The combination of the debit note and invoice can then be processed through the cost accounts. The accountant will of course await the receipt of the relevant credit note and adjustment of VAT from the supplier before finally agreeing the statement.

Procedure within the cost accounts
The copy invoices are initially sorted under project numbers and other cost centres such as the various overhead accounts, stores or plant department. The invoices for each project are then sub-sorted into cost categories such as materials, hired plant and special expenses.

At the end of each accounting period (calendar month) the invoices are then add-listed to provide a separate total for the sub-division of each project. The add-list can then be stapled to each batch of invoices for the accounting period as a permanent record and filed on a lever arch file for each contract. Other cost documentation such as wages, certified payments, etc., can be similarly filed and add-listed.

The total of the copy invoices and other cost documentation processed for each accounting period will be compared and reconciled with the total of the original invoices and other documentation processed via the financial accounts.

The total cost allocated to the various headings under each contract will be entered in a cost ledger as a permanent record each month.

The cost system outlined has certain definite advantages:

(a) It is simple to operate and easy to understand.
(b) Surveyors and management can have easy and direct access to analysed monthly costs recorded in a cost ledger as a single line entry for each contract every month. Any queries can be resolved by direct access to the original information on the project cost file, filed under cost headings in monthly batches.
(c) Any errors in costing, particularly invoices charged to the wrong project, are easy to identify and correct.
(d) All the cost information for a project is retained in one or a very small number of files.

The problem with such a system is that a more detailed breakdown of costs into trades, elements or work sections would be difficult to achieve on a manual basis. Management will therefore be dependent on surveying records, cost targets and the management accounts.

MORE COMPLEX COSTING SYSTEMS

There will be an obvious benefit to management if costs could be more directly related to work sections, elements, trades or individual bill of quantity items. With the rapid spread in the development and use of computer technology more complex costing systems are relatively simple to introduce, even in smaller building companies.

The checking of invoices will usually have to be undertaken manually. Once this has been completed each invoice or other costing document will need to be coded before being processed by the computer operator.

Coding

The code on each costing document will need to include the contract number and the work section, element, trade or bill of quantity reference. In addition it will almost certainly be necessary to give each document a unique reference number for ease of future identification and retrieval.

It is helpful if all orders are coded and, if possible, separate orders are used for different elements, work sections, etc. This will ensure that when the invoices are received they will be relatively easy to code and will not need splitting between different cost centres.

Cost breakdown

The decision as to how detailed a breakdown of costs is required is crucial and should only be taken at a high level in the management structure. The more detailed the cost breakdown and analysis, the more complex will become the coding and analytical decision-taking. It must be borne in mind that the majority of coding decisions will be taken by junior members of staff.

A well-thought-out cost breakdown and related coding system will enable costs to be reprocessed through the computer and presented to management in a variety of ways. For example, using the manual cost breakdown already discussed it would be possible to expand such a system to provide the following:

(a) A printout of costs in a simplified form, identical to that outlined for a manual system – directly employed labour, labour-only sub-contractors, etc.
(b) A breakdown of each cost heading in (a) above into trades, i.e., materials into concrete work, brickwork, etc., possibly using SMM classifications.

(c) A breakdown of the cost of each trade but with labour, materials and plant combined. This would compare directly with the breakdown of a traditional bill of quantities.

(d) A breakdown into elements – foundations, external walls, roofs, internal walls, etc., and subdivided again as in (b) or (c) above.

(e) A breakdown into work sections (groups of bill of quantity items) which would comprise an easily identifiable site operation.

(f) An analysed breakdown into individual sub-contract functions where sub-contractors are undertaking the bulk of the work.

In each case it may be possible to print out target costs against each subsection and therefore quantify any profit or loss. The advantages in such a system are obvious. Provided coding can be accurately and quickly undertaken cost records can be continuously and rapidly updated.

In order to achieve integration with financial accounts, invoices and other documentation should be processed in batches, possibly one day's output. This will enable the accounting staff to reconcile the totals of each batch on a daily basis.

Where the cost breakdown is sophisticated, problems may arise both on site and in the office. With many materials, for example cement, sand, aggregate, and bricks, the correct cost centre may be difficult to monitor. Such materials may be used in foundations, superstructure, roads, and drainage; if an elemental breakdown is employed, in a dozen different elements. It is therefore essential, if costs are to be meaningful, that site and surveying staff accurately monitor the flow of materials to each cost centre. This will obviously absorb management resources.

Retrieval and filing

Once invoices and other costing documentation have been correctly coded and costed via the computer system, management is faced with a choice of how to file the 'dead' paperwork:

(a) Filing could be on the basis of the unique number on each costing document. This would of course mean that the costing documentation processed for each day, week or month (depending on the size of the company) would not be split between individual contracts, development or overhead items, but filed in order of processing. In the event of an enquiry to identify the actual components of cost under an analysed heading, it may be essential to refer to the original documentation. The unique number, which must of course appear on the cost printout, will enable management to identify each individual docket but it may well be a laborious process to extract the costing details for one subsection of a project from the filing for the whole company. This does not compare with the ease of reference to actual original documentation in the manual system outlined earlier in this chapter.

(b) Filing could be either completely or partly broken down using the cost code on each document. Initially this could be on the basis of individual projects or overhead accounts and subsequently in as much detail as management consider necessary. The problem with undertaking filing on this basis is that accounting or management staff are in effect duplicating the process undertaken by the computer.

The problem with analysed costing in the building industry is that with the complexity and nature of the construction process, errors may well be frequent. The propensity for errors to occur must be balanced against the necessity for both management and surveying staff to have a reasonable degree of trust in the analysed cost figures produced. The identification and correction of coding errors may be virtually impossible unless either a cost centre is obviously incorrect or a fairly detailed manual backup, such as is outlined in (b) above, is utilised. Nevertheless, the advantages from a correctly administered costing system cannot be overemphasised. It is possible that, in future computer costing systems, a micro-film record of each document could be retained within the computer system and extracted on demand when required.

Even in small companies computers are an essential tool, particularly in the preparation of estimates and in pricing bills of quantities, where extensive calculations are involved. They can also be utilised in programming work including network analysis and critical path. Once computers have been introduced to a company and are found to be indispensable in these areas, it is a small step to progress to analysed costing.

MANAGEMENT ACCOUNTS

Management accounts may perhaps be viewed as the natural development from the financial accounts and cost accounts, and in fact draw on both. Generally the management accounts provide the necessary information to plan and control the business.

The company is not required by law or accountants and auditors to provide management accounts and they are only prepared at the discretion of the company. The management accountant will use the financial accounts and to a greater extent the cost accounts to prepare the necessary financial information for management decisions. It is therefore absolutely essential that the management accountant is aware of the implications of the weaknesses, strengths and accuracy of the cost accounts.

For many builders the instigation to prepare management accounts arises not from within their own organisation but from the insistence by external bodies that more detailed information concerning the company's financial position should be made available. This may stem from banks when negotiating overdrafts, from insurance companies when arranging for bonds, or from potential clients who wish to establish the financial integrity of the company before commencement of the tendering process. Perhaps the banks will be the most insistent on the provision of certain defined management accounting information on a regular basis.

Setting budgets and the associated budgetary control is one essential ingredient not only in ensuring that managers are aware of the financial implications of their decisions, but also in the measurement of actual performance against a predetermined target. It also enables management to anticipate both beneficial and adverse trends before the event or take evasive action when the evidence of an emerging problem has only just presented itself.

For most builders management accounting will be limited to the production of a few fundamental sets of additional information, although the national contractors will have developed many finely tuned and sophisticated management accounting techniques.

The medium-sized builder will need to provide certain basic information for the bank if any appreciable funding is necessary, including:

- Cash flow forecast or cash budget.
- Schedule of stocks of land and property, showing basic financial information including the planning position, cost, current market value, and anticipated start date on site. In the financial accounts, of course, land will usually be stated at the lower of cost or net realisable value.
- Profit forecast on contracting and development operations, prepared using the cost value reconciliation process as a base.

In addition, most companies will produce an overhead budget and allocate responsibility for its monitoring and control. It is also important for building companies to attempt to assess the correct allocation of overheads in the management accounts against each project to ascertain the true profit. This is necessary because many overhead costs are not included in work in progress but are written off against current profits each year (see Chapter 11).

It could also be argued that the preparation and monitoring of cost targets for trades, work sections or individual sub-contractors should be treated as part of the management accounts.

In effect, each builder has a choice in the level of sophistication and extent of the information that is considered necessary to plan and control his business. Financial accounts must be produced, cost accounts are almost essential for survival, and management accounts are a key ingredient to safe expansion.

10 Valuation of Construction Work

INTRODUCTION

In this chapter the various methods used in the valuation of construction work are examined and an assessment made of the accuracy that can be achieved. Chapter 11 is concerned with the problems associated with the comparison of value and cost and Chapter 12 with the implication of the resulting profit or loss on the valuation of work in progress included in the financial accounts of the company.

It has been said that 'a cynic knows the price of everything and the value of nothing'. This, of course, is using the term 'value' in the philosophical sense. In the construction industry, value is the estimation of the worth of either the completed building or the work in progress expressed in money terms. Actual prices will depend partly on the value of money itself. In times of inflation prices may rise because money is falling in value but the relative value of one building compared with another will remain unchanged.

The surveyor or valuer involved in the valuation of construction work must take account of the 'worth' of the building in relation to the status of the individual who requests the valuation. For example, a client may enter into a contract with a builder to construct a house in the Hebrides. The contract sum which would represent the value to the builder may be £50 000. The market value if the property had to be sold may only be £30 000. The valuation for fire insurance, however, may well be approaching £60 000.

The market value itself will reflect the way in which a purchaser views the completed building. In each case the actual price paid will be influenced by supply and demand.

(a) The building may be utilised for personal occupation, with the associated social or commercial benefits.

(b) The building could be viewed as an investment capable of yielding an income or annual return.

(c) The building could be viewed as a speculative purchase with an ultimate view to selling at a higher price, either at some future time, or after adaptation, conversion or change of use.

This chapter is primarily concerned with the valuation of work in progress on construction projects, and not the valuation of completed buildings.

ALTERNATIVE METHODS OF VALUATION

VALUATION BASED ON BILL OF QUANTITIES

Building work undertaken for a client and subject to standard forms of building contract, such as JCT 80, may be with or without bills of quantities.

Where bills of quantities are provided it is the duty of the client's quantity surveyor to ascertain the amount due to the contractor from the employer at each interim valuation of the work. The valuation is usually prepared on site at monthly intervals at a joint meeting of the client's quantity surveyor and the contractor's surveyor.

The client's quantity surveyor when preparing the valuation will invariably use the bill of quantities as the basis for calculating the amount due. The valuation will include preliminaries, measured work, provisional work, nominated sub-contractors and suppliers, materials on site, variations, claims and, where provided for in the contract, fluctuations. In effect each valuation should be based on the latest estimate of the final account including the builder's profit and overheads. The gross value of the work so calculated will be subject to a retention at the agreed contract percentage, usually between 3% and 5%. Once the quantity suveyor has ascertained the amount due to the contractor the architect will issue the interim certificate.

When valuing the work for the purpose of interim payments, the client's quantity surveyor is not expected or required to ensure that the valuation is absolutely accurate. In practice the usual approach is to ensure that every reasonable precaution is taken to avoid any obvious overpayment and the tendency is to undervalue rather than overvalue the work. Moreover, the client's quantity surveyor is not normally aware that any particular valuation may be of special significance or importance to the contractor, and ultimately the auditors, for calculating the value of work in progress at the end of the builder's financial year.

In view of the importance of valuations based on bills of quantities, the constituent elements of such valuations and the propensity for errors to occur are discussed later in this chapter.

VALUATION WITHOUT BILLS OF QUANTITIES

Where construction work is undertaken for an employer and quantities do not form part of the contract, various methods of valuation may be used. These valuations may be prepared for internal management purposes only, or as the basis of calculating the amount due from the employer at the period of the interim payment certificate. In the case of development projects, where the builder is undertaking the work himself, internal valuation will be essential for cost value reconciliation purposes and will take place at possibly monthly or, more commonly, three-monthly intervals.

There are numerous methods of valuation, but the most commonly used are a valuation based on original estimate, related to project progress, or based on estimated cost of completion. These will now be discussed in detail.

VALUATION BASED ON ORIGINAL ESTIMATE

Where bills of quantities are not provided the builder, in preparing his tender or feasibility study for development projects, will have taken off from the drawings and specification approximate or possibly detailed quantities which when priced will constitute the basis for preparing the estimate. These internal priced quantities do not form part of any contract and therefore any errors they contain will not be subject to adjustment in the final account and recovery from the client.

The valuation should be based upon the latest estimate of the final account and include measured work, materials on site and, if applicable, nominated sub-contractors and suppliers, variations and fluctuations. In the case of development projects profit and overheads may be excluded from the internal valuation in order that estimated cost can be directly compared with actual cost.

Comments made later in this chapter on the accuracy achieved when valuing the constituent elements of a valuation using bills of quantities apply equally to valuations based on the original estimate. In addition valuations based on the original estimate are more prone to error because:

(a) The valuation may not be verified by a quantity surveyor, and even where it is verified, the quantity surveyor only has access to such information as is supplied by the builder.
(b) The quantities prepared internally by the contractor's surveyor may only be approximate, or less accurate than those prepared by the client's quantity surveyor. Conversely, it is of course possible that very accurate and precise quantities may be available.
(c) The contractor's surveyor may be under pressure to obtain as much cash as possible at each valuation, and overvalue the work in progress at every opportunity. Without an external basis for valuation, the probability of such overvaluation being overlooked by the certifying officer, and in due course the contractor's auditor, is of course increased.

VALUATION RELATED TO PROJECT PROGRESS

The contract with a client or the mortgage deed for project finance for development may provide for the work to be valued not at regular intervals of time, but related to the stage reached in the construction process. In such cases valuation payments may be predetermined as a percentage of the contract sum or sale price. In the construction of an individual house, for example, stage payments could be agreed as:

Stage 1 – completion of substructure	25%
Stage 2 – roof tiling complete	50%
Stage 3 – plastering complete	75%
Stage 4 – house completed	100%

Such arrangements are common where banks or building societies are involved in funding the project. The obvious advantage is that each stage of the work can be clearly identified by a layman with limited knowledge or experience of the industry. Where interim payments are predetermined in this way they are unlikely to accurately reflect the actual value of the work completed at each stage. Therefore if this method is to be used to value work in progress, additional clearly identified payment stages should be introduced and calculations made to ensure that the percentage set against each stage accurately reflects the value of the work. The propensity for builders to overvalue at every opportunity in order to improve cash flow cannot of course be ignored.

VALUATION BASED ON ESTIMATED COST OF COMPLETION

Where the sale price or contract value is known it may on occasion prove both prudent and more accurate to calculate the estimated cost that will be incurred to complete the project and deduct this amount from the sale price to calculate the current valuation. The estimate should include any associated profit and overheads. This method of calculation will be useful in a variety of circumstances, particularly when the contract is nearing completion. The most important use, however, is in the case of residential development, where the sale price, and therefore the value of work in progress, is varying with market conditions. When sale prices are falling the valuation of work in progress prepared by this method often quickly drops below current costs.

To achieve reasonable accuracy, care must be taken to avoid underestimation of cost and to prepare a careful check-list of all outstanding work including maintenance and remedial work.

VALUATION AT COST

The Statement of Standard Accounting Practice no. 9, Stocks and Work in Progress introduces the concept of valuation at cost; this is discussed in detail in Chapter 12.

VALUATION AT NET REALISABLE VALUE

Net realisable value is defined in SSAP9 as 'the amount at which it is expected that items of stock and work in progress can be disposed of without creating either profit or loss in the year of sale' and, more particularly, as the actual or estimated selling price less all further costs to completion and all costs to be incurred in marketing and selling.

In effect, to arrive at a figure for net realisable value on a construction project, the builder must value his work in progress net (by deducting profit from the normal gross valuation) and then also deduct allowances for remedial work, estimated future losses, and provision for any costs likely to arise in the defects liability period.

VALUATION OF COMPLETED BUILDINGS

All the valuation methods so far referred to relate to the valuation of buildings in the course of construction or at completion before sales proceeds have been received. The valuation of land and property is discussed in Chapter 8.

VALUATION FOR FIRE INSURANCE

When valuing buildings for the purpose of fire insurance the valuation must include not only the replacement cost of the building at current rates, but also an allowance for inflation, demolition, removal of debris, and architect's and surveyors' fees. A possible credit might be included for salvage materials. The actual premium charged by the insurance company will depend upon the location of the building, the form of construction, and the use to which the building is put.

Fire insurance valuations are directly linked to the cost of construction and may therefore differ widely from the market value of the building, particularly with older properties and in areas where market values are depressed.

CONSTITUENT ELEMENTS OF THE VALUATION

Where bills of quantities are part of the contract documents they will inevitably form the basis of the quantity surveyor's valuation of work in progress. It is therefore important that examination is made of the practical implications of the steps involved. The majority of comments made would apply equally to valuations based on an original estimate or an internal bill of quantities.

The client's quantity surveyor will prepare the valuation under a number of headings including preliminaries, measured work (builder's work), materials on site, nominated sub-contractors and suppliers, day work, provisional sums and provisional work, variations, fluctuations and claims. The degree of accuracy of the valuation achieved by the client's quantity surveyor will vary between these various elements. This is particularly important when considering the adjustments that are necessary before reconciliation can be made with the cost records. The valuation prepared by the client's quantity surveyor is usually known as the 'external valuation'. The contractor's surveyor will normally be responsible for correcting and amending the external valuation in order to achieve a higher degree of accuracy. This amended valuation is known as the 'internal valuation'.

PRELIMINARIES

The preliminary section in a bill of quantities usually relates to items which will not form part of the permanent building work and are therefore excluded from the measured work. The builder when pricing the bill of quantities may treat the preliminary section in a variety of ways:

(a) Profit may be included in the measured rates or alternatively all or part of the profit may be set against specific items in the preliminary bill, for example site foremen or water for the works.
(b) Plant may be included wholly in the measured rates, wholly in the preliminaries, or partly in both. It is, for example, common practice to price the mixer for the brickwork in the measured rates but scaffolding, tower cranes and hoist in the preliminaries.
(c) The preliminaries may be priced on a calculated and factual basis. Equally the builder may use percentage or lump sum assessments of cost spread at random against a limited number of preliminary items.
(d) At tender stage the measured rates in the bill of quantities will be priced and extended and any adjustments when the tender is adjudicated are added to or omitted from the preliminaries bill.
(e) The builder may load or weight certain items in the preliminary bill with the objective of improving cash flow or safeguarding profit.
(f) The builder may omit to price many items even though they have cost implications.
(g) The preliminary bill may be unpriced or only partly priced and the cost of preliminaries transferred totally or partially to the measured rates as a deliberate pricing policy.

It is, therefore, apparent that in many cases the pricing of the preliminary bill may provide little indication of the actual cost of any particular item. The relative financial importance of preliminaries varies both between contracts of the same contractor and different building companies. From Building Cost Information Service records it can be shown that preliminaries may represent from 8% to 25% of project costs, with corresponding importance when considering the accuracy of interim valuations.

When preparing the interim valuation for a contract the client's quantity surveyor has to decide which method of assessing the preliminaries should be adopted. Often this is a point of conflict between the client's quantity surveyor and the contractor's surveyor, as widely different results may be obtained. On the initial assumption that the builder has calculated the preliminaries on a factual basis, the three basic methods of valuation are as follows.

Time basis
The total cost of the preliminaries in the bill of quantities is divided by the

number of months in the contract period and equal payments made at each monthly valuation. In the event of a contract running behind programme, or an extension of time being granted by the architect, the quantity surveyor will usually amend the valuation accordingly by averaging the payments over the extended period. In certain circumstances additional preliminaries may be paid to compensate the contractor when the contract period is extended.

Percentage basis

The total cost of the preliminaries is calculated as either a percentage of the contract sum or the value of measured work in the bill (excluding prime cost – PC – and provisional sums). At each interim valuation the relevant percentage is applied to the value of either the builder's work or the total measured work completed, in order to assess the value of the preliminaries.

Price basis

The preliminaries are valued in accordance with the specific pricing in the bill of quantities. Items such as site huts, water for the works, and the site foreman, are valued on a time basis, but other items which arise at a particular point in the contract programme, such as scaffolding, are included in the valuation as and when the respective item is executed on site.

When the client's quantity surveyor values the preliminaries on a time or percentage basis it is a simple matter to administer, but at any particular point during the contract the calculated amount of the preliminaries is unlikely to accurately reflect the cost and therefore the amount due. Valuation on either of these bases is sufficiently accurate for interim valuations on the majority of contracts. Valuation on a priced basis, however, should be much more accurate provided that the builder has correctly estimated and priced the preliminaries at tender stage. Unfortunately, as discussed earlier, the builder may for a variety of reasons fail to price the preliminaries accurately. Moreover, many builders attempt to front-end load the preliminaries bill by overpricing certain items in anticipation that the client's quantity surveyor will value on a priced basis with consequential overvaluation and improved cash flow. For this reason many quantity surveyors are reluctant to accept the pricing of the builder unless detailed breakdowns are provided of the relevant items in the preliminaries bill.

The client's quantity surveyor will inevitably use his judgement and professional expertise to protect as far as possible the interest of the client and ensure that at each valuation the amount allowed for preliminaries represents a fair and equitable proportion of the gross valuation. In practice, for all of the reasons discussed, it will be essential for the builder to look closely at the valuation of the preliminaries, and possibly make substantial adjustments in order that the internal valuation is an accurate assessment to date for cost value reconciliation purposes.

MEASURED WORK

The measured or builder's work comprises the measured items, forming the bulk of the bill of quantities, but excluding PC and provisional sums and the preliminaries. The client's quantity surveyor when preparing this part of the valuation will usually examine each item in the bill to establish if the work has been completed on site. Where an item is only partially complete, one of the following procedures will be adopted:

- A percentage assessment will be made.
- The amount of work completed will be measured and valued.
- When an item is nearing completion a deduction can be made for the quantity of work outstanding.

An alternative to this item by item assessment is to take a combination of items in work sections, or trades, and again value on a measured or percentage basis. Where the client's quantity surveyor is preparing valuations for large housing schemes and a substantial amount of repetition is involved it is common practice to prepare a breakdown of the priced bill of quantities for each house type into easily identifiable stages in the construction process. The corresponding value will be shown for each stage with a blank column for the current month's figures. The use of stages in preparing the valuation reduces the possibility of errors occurring and the result achieved is usually reasonably accurate. The client's quantity surveyor may often adopt a conservative approach and only include a stage when the work is completed, thus marginally undervaluing the work in progress.

To value the builder's work precisely can be both difficult and time-consuming and the quantity surveyor's judgement at each valuation will probably be subject to a marginal error of plus or minus 5%.

PROVISIONAL WORK

Where at tender stage the client's quantity suveyor is uncertain of the actual quantities of the work to be executed, for example in substructure or builder's work in association with services, it is normal practice to estimate the quantities and mark the relevant items in the bill as 'provisional'.

The client's quantity surveyor should measure and evaluate such items as the work proceeds in order that an accurate assessment can be made at each interim valuation. Under pressure of circumstances remeasurement may be delayed until the final account stage and the valuation will therefore probably be based on the provisional quantities in the bill. This will almost certainly, of course, lead to under- or overvaluation. The author is reminded of one case where the substructure was all provisional and the client's quantity surveyor used the bill of quantities as the basis of valuation. The bill was front-end loaded and the substructure rates therefore somewhat higher than would normally be expected. The foundations when remeasured at final account stage revealed a dramatic omission of approximately 10% of the contract sum, and the builder had in fact been substantially overpaid. When the final account was presented by the client's quantity surveyor to the builder (two years after practical completion) the builder repaid the client the amount of the overpayment. Instances such as this are rare; it is more common for provisional work to be undervalued prior to the issue of the penultimate or final certificate.

MATERIALS ON SITE

Accurate valuation of materials on site by the client's quantity surveyor is rarely achieved. Frequently the quantity of unfixed material will be calculated using the delivery records of the contractor's surveyor or site agent as a base figure and deducting the quantities of materials built into the work. Alternatively a complete list of materials on site may be supplied by the builder and possibly checked by the client's quantity surveyor or clerk of works.

The client's quantity surveyor will calculate the value of the materials by reference to the basic price list if available, the actual prices on the contractors' invoices, or current market prices as published in trade journals, always of course keeping in mind the rate for executed work quoted by the contractor in the bill. When making the assessment the quantity surveyor should (but often may not) make due allowance for waste, theft, double-handling, damage, over-ordering, inadequate storage, and deterioration. Care should also be taken not to overlook high cost but small items such as manhole covers, screws, and other fixings and ironmongery. Strictly speaking the client's quantity surveyor should either prepare his own schedule or carry out a detailed physical check of the actual materials on site, making any necessary adjustments for waste, double-handling, etc.

Clause 30.2.1.2 of JCT 80 states that the total value of the unfixed materials and goods delivered to or adjacent to the works may only be included in the valuation if they are 'reasonably properly and not prematurely so delivered and are adequately protected against weather and other casualties'. The client's quantity surveyor should, therefore, be alert to the need to exclude materials from the valuation where they have been delivered too early in the contract programme. Occasionally the builder may use the site to store surplus materials from other projects which cannot be utilised in the work. Care should be taken to ensure that such materials are not included in the valuation.

NOMINATED SUB-CONTRACTORS AND SUPPLIERS

The builder will usually advise the nominated sub-contractors of the approximate dates of monthly valuation in order that their accounts can be submitted in time for inclusion in the interim valuation. It is important that the nominated sub-contractors' accounts, which may well include materials on site, additional work and possibly increased costs, are carefully checked and site measurements taken if necessary. Where both the client's quantity surveyor and contractor's surveyor lack the necessary expert knowledge to evaluate the sub-contract work, particularly with regard to services, it is preferable that the account be referred to the appropriate consultant concerned for expert vetting and approval.

The amount certified to any particular sub-contractor may therefore not reflect the amount claimed by that sub-contractor. Nominated sub-contractors on occasion overvalue the work in progress in anticipation that it may prove possible to improve their cash flow. The contractor is only required to pay the amount certified less cash discount, unless the sub-contractor has raised in addition a claim against the builder for a loss or damage to the sub-contract works.

The client's architect or quantity surveyor will usually inform the nominated sub-contractor of the amount included for him in the interim certificate, together with the dates when he may expect payment.

Nominated suppliers' invoices should of course be checked with the order and delivery note in the usual way before inclusion in the interim valuation. It is also important for the client's quantity surveyor to verify that such materials are correctly stored and protected.

The valuation statement will usually show the payment position regarding each nominated sub-contractor and supplier, including the total certified to date, the amount previously certified and the amount certified in the current month. Most quantity surveyors will require the builder to produce evidence that the nominated sub-conractor has received payment for the previous months as certified.

At final account stage the prime cost sum in the bill of quantities will be omitted from the contract sum and the corresponding amounts paid or payable to the nominated sub-contractor or supplier substituted. Adjustment will also be made for cash discount, profit and, where applicable, attendance.

A prime cost sum is usually shown in the bill of quantities as:

Provide the sum of £ ... for work to be executed by a nominated sub-contractor.
Add for profit
Add for general attendance
Add for special attendance

Cash discount
Under the terms of JCT 80 the contractor is entitled to deduct a cash discount from the amounts due to nominated sub-contractors and suppliers at each interim valuation, provided payment is made within the agreed period. The cash discount for nominated sub-contractors is $2\frac{1}{2}\%$ and for nominated suppliers 5%. The government contract GC/Works/ 1 provides for a $2\frac{1}{2}\%$ cash discount in each case. Cash discounts in excess of these provisions, and any trade discounts, must be retained for the benefit of the employer.

Statutory undertakings such as the water authority, electricity and gas, carrying out work solely in pursuance of their statutory obligations, are not prepared, and as a consequence not required, to allow cash discounts to the contractor.

General contractor's profit

At tender stage the contractor is given the opportunity to price the profit usually as a percentage of the PC sum. At each interim valuation this percentage will be applied to the amounts certified and included in the valuation. If the profit is shown as a lump sum the valuation and ultimate final payment of profit will be adjusted on a pro rata basis. If the provision in the contract for payment of a nominated sub-contractor direct is invoked, the general contractor will still be entitled to payment of profit, but not of course the cash discount.

Attendance

The builder is also given the opportunity to price attendance on the sub-contractor in the bill. The Standard Method of Measurement in clauses B9.2 and 9.3 states that:

'1. An item shall be given in each case for general attendance which shall be deemed to include the use of the Contractor's temporary roads, pavings and paths, standing scaffolding, standing power operated hoisting plant, the provision of temporary lighting and water supplies, clearing away rubbish, provision of space for the sub-contractor's own offices and for the storage of his plant and materials and the use of messrooms, sanitary accommodation and welfare facilities.

2. Other attendance on nominated sub-contractors where required shall be described and given as an item in each case for:

(a) Special scaffolding or scaffolding additional to the Contractor's standing scaffolding.
(b) The provision of temporary access roads and hardstandings in connection with structural steelwork, precast concrete components, piling, heavy items of plant and the like.
(c) Unloading, distributing, hoisting and placing in position giving in the case of significant items the weight and/or size.
(d) The provision of covered storage and accommodation including lighting and power thereto.
(e) Power supplies giving the maximum load.
(f) Maintenance of specific temperature or humidity levels.
(g) Any other attendance not included in this clause or in clause B.9.2.'

The price inserted by the builder in the bill of quantities is usually treated as a lump sum and not adjusted pro rata to the actual cost of the sub-contract work. If, however, the nature of the sub-contract works was 'substantially' varied and the attendance affected, adjustment would be made on a pro rata basis. If the builder priced the attendance as a percentage this should be adjusted to a lump sum in the bill of quantities before the contract is signed. In the event of a percentage remaining in the contract document the attendance would have to be adjusted pro rata to the actual cost of the sub-contract works, assuming that this was the intention of the parties signing the contract. The client's quantity surveyor, when preparing the valuation, will usually calculate the attendance in direct proportion to the value of the sub-contractor's interim account. Obviously, however, this may not accurately reflect the actual cost incurred by the builder of attending on the sub-contractor at that point in the work.

PROVISIONAL SUMS AND VARIATIONS

Provisional sums may be included in the bills of quantities for work which cannot be entirely foreseen, defined, or detailed at the time the tendering documents are issued. Clause 13 of JCT 80 requires that the architect shall issue instructions regarding the expenditure of provisional sums and that the quantity surveyor, unless otherwise agreed by the employer and contractor, shall value the work in accordance with defined rules.

Clause 13.5 of JCT 80 provides that:

- Where the work is of a similar character to, is executed under similar conditions as, and does not significantly change the quantity of, work set out in the contract bills, the rates and prices for the work so set out shall determine the valuation.
- Where the work is of similar character to work set out in the contract bills but is not executed under similar conditions thereto and/or significantly changes the quantity thereof, the rates and prices for the work so set out shall be the basis for determining the valuation and the valuation shall include a fair allowance for such difference in conditions and/or quantity.
- Where the work is not of similar character to work set out in the contract bills the work shall be valued at fair rates and prices.

The architect may also issue instructions regarding any variations to the design, quality or quantity of the works as shown upon the contract drawings or included in the contract bills. The variation may result in an addition, omission or substitution of any work or an alteration to the specification of any materials or goods. Variations must also be issued where there is an addition, omission or alteration to any obligation or restriction imposed by the employer in the contract bills, such as access to any part of the site, limitations of working space or working hours, or execution or completion of the work in a specific order.

If the architect gives a verbal instruction which constitutes a variation the contractor should confirm the instruction in writing within seven days. If the architect does not dissent from the confirmation within a further seven days the instruction becomes an official variation order. Where a written confirmation of an instruction is received by the contractor before the expiration of this 14-day period the instruction will take effect from the date of the architect's confirmation. Where neither the architect nor contractor confirms instructions in writing but the contractor has nevertheless complied with such instructions, provided the architect confirms the instructions at any time prior to the issue of the final certificate, the variation will be deemed to have taken effect from the date of the original verbal instruction.

The contractor's surveyor must be given the opportunity of being present at the time the variations are measured and valued by the quantity surveyor. Variations should be valued in accordance with the rules outlined above for provisional sums.

The value of both variations and the expenditure related to provisional sums should be included in the interim valuation as part of the total value of work executed. It is essential that variations should be measured and priced and the resulting omission or addition included as soon as possible in the interim valuation to ensure an accurate assessment. It must be appreciated that there is often a tendency for such accurate measurement and valuation to be delayed by either the client's quantity surveyor or the contractor's surveyor or both until after practical completion of the work. During the intervening period the client's quantity surveyor will use an approximate estimate as the basis of each interim valuation. Although such practice may adequately meet the needs of both the client and his quantity surveyor, the actual valuation of the work from the contractor's point of view will tend to be inaccurate. Moreover, verbal instructions not confirmed in writing until late in the contract period will not be included in interim valuations.

FLUCTUATIONS
Where a contract is let on a 'fixed price' basis the builder will allow for any

possible fluctuations or increased cost of labour, materials and plant in the preliminaries. In such circumstances the fluctuations will be valued by one of the methods outlined earlier in this chapter in the section on preliminaries.

Provision may be made in the contract, however, for the builder to recover increased costs. Recovery will usually either be on the traditional basis or by the use of the formula method of reimbursement.

Traditional method

The traditional method of recovery of increased costs involves the use of a basic list. When the basic list is used it may well happen either by choice or negligence that the builder may omit many materials and therefore they will not qualify for adjustment. This may adversely affect the profit margin of the project. There is unfortunately a tendency for the increased cost recovery to be delayed until late in the contract period, or even left to the final account stage. This tendency is of course due to the large volume of work involved for the builder in the preparation of the claim for increased cost of labour and materials. Equally, the client's quantity surveyor will need many hours for checking. Ideally it is in the interest of all parties to the contract that full details scheduling the fluctuations claim together with original invoices and wage sheets, etc., should be provided by the builder and checked by the client's quantity surveyor at each interim valuation.

Under the terms of JTC 80 materials on site cannot be included in the calculation of fluctuations and payment would only be made to the builder when such materials are incorporated into the works. It is important to note that it is not always possible for the builder to recover all his increased costs. For example, builders may pay higher rates for labour than those officially recognised in the national rule agreement, or employ sub-contractors on enhanced rates. Similarly, during periods of material shortages builders may be forced to pay higher prices for imported materials than those prevailing in the UK.

Formula method

When the contract provides for increased costs to be adjusted using the NEDO (Osborne) or Baxter formula, the rules applying to their use are clearly defined. The amount of the claim by the builder will not relate to the actual cost of the fluctuations in labour, materials and plant on a contract but to a general indication of the overall level of construction cost. The cost indices are updated each month by the Property Services Agency (PSA) of the Department of the Environment. When these indices are published they are deemed provisional and firm indices are published three months later.

The base month used in the formula will usually be one month prior to the tender date and the idices for that month will be included in the contract conditions. At each valuation the period of the valuation is defined as commencing on the day following the date of the previous valuation, up to and including the date of the current valuation. The indices that will apply to the valuation are those for the month in which the mid-point of the valuation period occurs. Where the valuation period contains an even number of days the mid-point will be the middle day of the period remaining after deducting the last day. The monthly indices when published are classified in 48 work categories, and at each valuation the relevant measured work in the annotated bill of quantities must be divided into these work categories.

It is important that valuations should be as accurate as possible as formula calculations will not normally be amended at a later date. When mistakes in the valuation have occurred it may be possible to correct these retrospectively provided such adjustments are made before the firm index numbers have been substituted for the provisional indices. Errors in the actual calculations, however, must be adjusted immediately they have been identified.

It will be apparent that there is some advantage to the builder in arranging for the valuation dates to be just after the middle of each month so that the mid-point of the valuation period occurs in the first few days of the calendar month, thus maximising increased cost recovery.

It will also be apparent that the builder could decide to back-end load the prices in the bill of quantities at tender stage in order to delay payment for measured work and thus increase the fluctuations recovery when the formula is applied for monthly valuations. This tactic would of course have an adverse effect on cash flow but, on balance, a possible advantage in increased profit potential. Equally, as the value of unfixed materials and goods is not permitted to be included in the formula calculation until they have been incorporated in the work, it will be of benefit to the contractor to speculate with material prices. Where considered prudent, materials could be purchased and brought on site well before they are required in the contract programme. The builder will then receive the benefit of any increase in price that occurs if such increase arises before the material in question is incorporated in the work, particularly when inflation is running at a high level. The builder will of course run the risk of adverse cash flow problems as the client's quantity surveyor strictly should not include the value of such materials in the interim valuation if they are prematurely delivered to site.

ACCURACY OF THE VALUATION

It will be apparent when cost value reconciliation is considered in Chapter 11 that the accuracy of the valuation is of vital importance to the builder's surveyor, accountant and auditor in determining attributable profit and foreseeable losses on work in progress. The client's quantity surveyor when valuing the work for the purpose of interim payments is not expected or required to prepare a valuation which is absolutely accurate. The usual approach adopted by the client's quantity surveyor will be to take every reasonable precaution to avoid any obvious overpayment.

The client's quantity surveyor is not normally aware that any particular valuation for a project may be of any special significance to the builder and could be utilised by the builder's accountants and auditor for calculating the value of work in progress at the end of the builder's financial year. The builder's surveyor may prepare the valuation and forward the details to the client's quantity surveyor for vetting in anticipation of the site visit, or he may present details to the quantity surveyor on site. Occasionally, during the progress of a contract where such arrangements have become a routine, the client's quantity surveyor, through pressure of circumstances, may fail either to visit the site or to fully check the details submitted by the builder's surveyor. The valuation submitted by the builder and approved for payment by the client's quantity surveyor may of course be perfectly acceptable, but where the builder's surveyor is under pressure from management to obtain as much cash as possible at each valuation, overvaluation could easily occur.

Occasionally the valuation on site is prepared by an inexperienced junior or unqualified surveyor on behalf of the client's quantity surveyor responsible for the site. In such circumstances the likelihood of errors in the valuation may well be increased.

When the basis of preparing the valuation is the bill of quantities, it will be apparent from the brief analysis of the constitutent elements of the valuation outlined in this chapter that under- or overvaluation of at least 5% on any individual interim payment could easily arise. During the course of the work such under- or overvaluation will tend to be self-correcting and the percentage inaccuracy will be inclined to diminish as the contract approaches practical completion. In practice at this point most contracts will be slightly under-, rather than over-valued by the quantity surveyor, in anticipation of an accurate remeasurement and assessment of variations, provisional work, increased costs and claims at final account stage.

The marginal under- or overvaluation of the interim certificates of a contract will normally be of little significance to the client who has the additional protection of both the retention and the value of work completed during the period of up to three weeks' delay between the valuation and payment. (The architect must issue the interim certificate within seven days of the valuation by the quantity surveyor taking place and the contractor is entitled to payment by the employer within 14 days from the date of issue of each interim certificate.)

On the other hand, from the builder's point of view, when considering that net profits in the construction industry are in the order of 2% to 3% on turnover, an average of a $2\frac{1}{2}\%$ error in the interim valuation will dramatically distort estimated profits unless such errors are adjusted in the builder's internal valuation.

WEIGHTING
When the tender is in course of preparation it is possible or even probable that the estimator or management responsible for tender submission may adjust the pricing of the bill of quantities in anticipation of achieving an improved financial return on the project. The adjustment to the pricing of the bills will not affect the overall tender price because any adjustments to individual rates will be compensated for elsewhere in the bill. Once the bill of quantities has been included as part of the contract documents the bill rates become contract rates and will be utilised by the client's quantity surveyor for both the preparation of interim valuations and the remeasurement of any provisional work or variation orders. At tender stage, however, the quantity surveyor does have an opportunity of examining the priced bills and advising both the builder and client of the possible financial implications of any rates which appear to be loaded. It is possible, after consultation with the builder, that the rates concerned may be adjusted. In practice, however, the quantity surveyor will be hard pressed to identify weighted items or even prove that weighting has occurred, as the under- or overpricing of the individual rates will usually be marginal.

Weighting can be classified under three headings: front-end loading, back-end loading, and errors.

Front-end loading

Front-end loading occurs when profit and costs are transferred from items occurring late in the contract programme and concentrated on early site operations or 'safe' items in the preliminaries. The effect of such adjustments is that when the work in progress is valued in the early valuations on a project the contractor will receive enhanced payments. This overpayment will in due course be compensated by reduced payments at the end of the contract. The accumulative effect of such adjustments will of course be to substantially improve the builder's cash flow, as overpayment will occur throughout virtually the whole contract period. It is possible for builders, including national companies, to perfect this technique to the point where surplus funds are released by the contracting operations of the company to fund residential, industrial, or commercial development or other activities.

Where a contract is let on a fluctuating basis and increased costs are to be adjusted using the NEDO forumula, front-end loading will result in a substantial under-recovery of increased costs. In these circumstances the builder will be faced with a choice between improved cash flow and reduced profitability.

Back-end loading

The introduction of increased costs recovery using a formula price adjustment has resulted in some builders transferring costs and profit to items occurring late in the contract programme, and the equivalent reductions being made in early operations. This technique results in the work being undervalued throughout the contract period, and this undervaluation being made good towards completion. Over-recovery of increased cost occurs, with a consequent improvement in project profit. Cash flow will of course be adversely affected. The builder will need to be well briefed with regard to the commodity market in order to be able to identify the materials most likely to provide the greatest return in order that weighting occurs on those items in the bill of quantities.

Errors

At tender stage it is possible that the estimator or management may identify inaccuracies in the bill of quantities. JCT80 provides that errors in quantities shall be corrected and treated as a variation. In circumstances where the quantities in the bill are less than shown on the drawings the builder may well price the item at a higher rate than normal. Equally, where the quantities are overmeasured the item will be priced at a lower rate than normal. As previously mentioned, the client's quantity surveyor when vetting the bill of quantities should spot any obvious tampering with the rates, but adjustments of up to 30% above or below the norm may be difficult to identify. If the rates are not amended by the client's quantity surveyor before the contract is signed the builder will of course gain financially when the errors are adjusted.

Genuine errors in pricing may also occur. When these items are included in the interim valuation distortion in the profit or loss at any given point in the contract may well result.

RISKS IN WEIGHTING

In applying the tactics of weighting to a contract the builder will not necessarily always achieve the anticipated improved financial return. The practice has inherent risks and weaknesses, particularly where variations occur in quantities. For example, if the quantity of an item which has been priced at an enhanced rate is reduced, the builder will lose the proportional part of the tranferred cost or profit. On the other hand if the quantities of the same item are increased the builder will make substantial additional gains, provided the variation rules in the contract are not breached. Equally, when items in the bill have been under-priced and the quantities are varied, the builder will either be obliged to carry out additional work at a loss or, where quantities are reduced, the omission to the contract sum will be less than should be the case, thus resulting in increased profits. The contractor at tender stage must therefore of necessity carefully examine the probability that items affected by weighting will be subject to variation, and only amend the most stable items in the bill.

On balance many builders would consider that the probability of variations occurring to weighted items is equally liable to result in under- as over-recovery. In fact, if the substructure is weighted, the probability on the majority of contracts is that quantities will tend to increase rather than decrease thus tipping the scales slightly in the builder's favour.

The valuations will of course be based on the bill of quantities and any form of weighting or error will distort both individual and accumulative valuations. It is therefore important that the builder keeps careful records of all items that are amended at tender stage in order to calculate the internal valuation accurately.

11 Cost Value Reconciliation

INTRODUCTION

In Chapter 9 the various methods by which a builder calculates construction costs were discussed. In Chapter 10 the various methods of valuation of building work and the levels of accuracy likely to be achieved were outlined. Management in the construction industry will be concerned to compare value with cost, with the objective of identifying the profit to date on individual contracts. The responsibility for this comparison or reconciliation (CVC or CVR) varies from company to company, but the builder's surveyor is likely to be a central figure. Assistance in the preparation of CVR will usually be provided by site or contract management and the company's accounts department. In view of the diverse opinions regarding certain aspects of CVR it is important that more than one person is involved in its preparation and that a balanced, prudent viewpoint prevails. Moreover, it is essential that those responsible for the preparation of CVR are aware of all the implications concerning the accuracy of costs, valuation and the requirements of SSAP9.

Perhaps the greatest problem facing the builder is the attitude to be taken regarding the confidentiality of profits or losses revealed by the CVR process. The majority of builders maintain tight security and only reveal the profit margins on contracts or development to directors and senior management. In any event the profits or losses revealed by the CVR process do not necessarily take account of unallocated overheads which form part of a separate calculation. In order to overcome this problem some companies add a fixed overhead percentage to CVR results, probably in excess of actual overhead levels, thus depressing profits or increasing losses. This distorted result is declared to the more junior levels of management. Such a policy, provided the percentage is not too overstated, may encourage staff to work towards achieving a good margin on the project notwithstanding the overhead surcharge.

However, if the overheads are too overloaded this may result in management giving up, and lacking in enthusiasm.

The reconciliation of cost and valuation should take place on a regular basis, usually monthly, to coincide with either the availability of cost figures or current valuation – preferably both. On very large projects the builder may opt to prepare cost value reconciliations at shorter intervals, say every two weeks. Smaller companies, however, with limited resources, may only undertake the exercise once or twice a year, to coincide with the half-yearly or annual accounts.

The size and structure of construction companies will influence not only the frequency of preparation of cost value reconciliation statements, but also the probability that accurate and meaningful figures will be produced. From the study of costing and methods of valuation it is clear that the likelihood of errors occurring is high. It will therefore be apparent that a simple comparison of cost to date and value to date will not indicate a realistic assessment of profit or loss on work in progress. Adjustments will therefore be necessary to both cost and valuation figures in order that an accurate comparison can be made.

Different companies adopt alternative methods of undertaking these adjustments. In some cases it would be possible to adjust either the cost or the valuation and the calculated profit would be the same. The most important factor is that management have the necessary proficiency and expertise in both surveying and accountancy.

ADJUSTMENT TO COST

When costing was considered in chapter 9 it was emphasised that the cost accounts must be reconciled and balanced with the financial accounts and that consequently project costs are a proven and reliable record. The cost for each project will normally be available every month following the close down of the costing and financial accounts.

There will be an obvious advantage if the builder's surveyor makes every endeavour to ensure that monthly valuations coincide as nearly as possible with the company's accounting period. If this can be achieved it will substantially reduce adjustments to either the cost or valuation of any work executed during the intervening period.

The majority of quantity surveyors are helpful in arranging valuations to suit the requirements of the builder but in the final analysis the architect has the power to decide the dates of the interim certificates, although they must be issued thereafter at the period of interim certificates stated in the contract, usually monthly. As previously mentioned, there is some advantage to the builder when undertaking a fluctuating contract using the NEDO formula to arrange valuations just after the middle of the month. The close down date for the cost accounts for the majority of builders, however, is at the end of the calendar month. There will therefore be a substantial adjustment to cost in such circumstances.

In addition to this adjustment certain routine adjustments will need to be made to cost figures before cost value reconciliation can take place.

MATERIAL INVOICES NOT ISSUED

When the interim valuation is prepared by the client's quantity surveyor, materials incorporated into the work or stored on site will be included in the detailed make-up of the valuation. The relevant invoices for such materials, however, may not necessarily have been raised by the supplier or indeed received by the builder, and consequently they will be excluded from the cost accounts.

The builder's accountant will probably be unaware of such invoices unless delivery tickets are accurately monitored and reconciled on a monthly basis. The surveyor or accountant will need to prepare a schedule of accruals in order that the cost provided by the accounts department may be adjusted to match the relevant valuation.

LATE MATERIAL INVOICES

Materials may have been included in the valuation but the relevant invoices may only have been received by the company after the close down of the monthly cost accounts. Such invoices, although excluded from the cost accounts, can usually be easily identified by the accountant or surveyor and an addendum of late cost prepared. Many larger companies operate a site costing system separately from the official company costing administered by the accounts department. These systems provide not only a rapid and more immediate guide to project costs, but also a useful check and backup when identifying delayed or late invoices. The nature of site costing, however, may well lead to inaccuracies, and frequent reconciliation with the official cost records is essential.

PLANT COSTS

Where plant is hired externally similar problems to those outlined above for delayed and late material invoices will also apply to plant invoices. In fact it is probably more common for plant invoices to be delayed as some hire companies delay raising the invoice until the plant is taken off hire. In addition delivery and collection charges may distort the true cost at any particular point in time. Moreover, the builder may be contra-charged for any losses or damage to mechanical plant including tyres. It is essential that the condition of plant is checked both on arrival and when leaving the site and the accounts department advised of any extra costs likely to arise. It is also important to note the date plant is received and taken off hire.

The hire rate for non-mechanical plant, particularly scaffolding, may also be subject to substantial surcharges where the builder has lost boards or fittings. Invariably some damage or loss occurs and the cost will only be revealed after the plant has been returned to the hiring company. On projects where long periods of hire are anticipated, regular stock-taking should take place on site to identify levels of loss and damage.

The formal cost system of the company will only cost invoices received and it is therefore essential that the surveyor makes full provision for anticipated losses and damage and any adjustments for distortions or late costs.

Where plant is hired internally the accounts department will be aware of the accuracy of the costing system and any distortions in cost or profit on internal plant hire. However, care should be taken by site staff to identify and account for any losses or damage to internal plant.

LABOUR COSTS

Directly employed labour is usually costed on a weekly basis (see chapter 9). These costs may therefore be slightly undervalued at the time of the monthly closedown and will need minor amendments to calculate the adjustment necessary to update the labour costs to the same day as that of the valuation.

Labour-only sub-contract payments, on the other hand, and their respective costing, are much more likely to be inaccurate for a variety of reasons:

(a) The accountant will use the payment certificate or sub-contractor's request for payment as the costing document. As discussed in Chapter 9, only those costing documents applicable to the calendar month will be included in the monthly cost close down. Unless, therefore, the valuation and the assessment of the sub-contractor's work takes place on the nearest working day to the end of the calendar month, there will inevitably be minor inaccuracies in the cost. Adjustment for any divergence can easily be made on a pro rata basis.

(b) The measurement of the work of labour-only sub-contractors was discussed in detail in Chapter 6. Whichever method of valuation is used it is unlikely that the valuation will be absolutely accurate. In fact many of the factors affecting the accuracy of the builder's valuation will apply equally to sub-contractors. Frequently the sub-contractor will attempt to improve his cash flow by overvaluation. Often, intermediate valuations are only approximate, accurate remeasurement being left until either the whole, or a defined section, of the sub-contract work is complete. Generally, however, both labour-only sub-contractors and the builder are concerned to maintain reasonably accurate valuations and it will be the responsibility for the builder's surveyor to maintain a high standard of valuation.

(c) Difficulties may arise where a sub-contractor has claims against the builder which have not been settled. In these circumstances the amount of the claim must be added to the adjusted cost.

(d) Daywork costs which arise on labour-only sub-contractors must be closely monitored as such costs are often unrecoverable at final account stage. It is essential, therefore, that a financial provision is made.

LABOUR AND MATERIAL SUB-CONTRACTORS
Costing documentation for labour and material sub-contractors may be raised weekly, monthly or at the completion of the work. It is very likely, therefore, that costing will not relate to the date of the valuation. The comments made regarding labour-only sub-contractors apply equally to labour and material sub-contractors.

NOMINATED SUB-CONTRACTORS AND SUPPLIERS
The payment procedure and associated costing for nominated sub-contractors and suppliers will normally only be initiated *after* the architect's certificate has been received by the builder. This will be between 7 and 14 days following the date of the valuation by the client's quantity surveyor. The resulting payment certificate from the builder to the nominated sub-contractor or supplier may well only be raised after

the close of the accounting period and will therefore be excluded from the current month's costing. The relevant costs will therefore be included in the following month.

It is a relatively simple matter to identify the total costs that should be attributed to both nominated sub-contractors and suppliers from the valuation. Before the cost records are adjusted to provide the correct cost for the accounting period, any claims or charges levied against the builder but not chargeable to the client should be incorporated. It is also important to note that the amount included in the interim certificate paid to the sub-contractor or supplier and subsequently costed may not be in accordance with any payment request received.

RESERVES
Although the cost records may be accurate at any particular point in the contract period, provision should be made for any possible future liabilities not recoverable under the contract, such as site clearance, and remedial work during the defects liability period. Foreseeable losses on future work caused for example by incorrect estimating, winter working or shortfall in recovery of increased costs, are dealt with in Chapter 12.

ADJUSTMENTS TO THE VALUATION

In Chapter 10 reference was made to the accuracy of the valuation prepared by the clients' quantity surveyor, and the problems of utilising such external valuations for cost value reconciliation purposes.

INTERNAL VALUATION
The majority of national contractors make provision on their cost value reconciliation format for an adjustment to the valuation to compensate for any deliberate or accidental errors and weighting. In addition, each aspect of the valuation previously identified (preliminaries, measured work, materials on site, attendance on nominated sub-contractors, provisional work, variations, fluctuations, weighting, front- and back-end loading, and pricing errors) will need examination and appraisal. The necessary adjustments must then be made to the external valuation which will form the basis of the cost value reconciliation.

VALUATIONS OUT OF SEQUENCE WITH THE CLOSE OF THE ACCOUNTING PERIOD

In Chapter 9 the importance of the integration of the cost and financial accounts was emphasised and this integration requires that a monthly accounting period is recognised and established. The majority of companies close down both the costs and financial accounts on the last day of each calendar month. The builder's surveyor will usually arrange the valuation date to coincide, as nearly as possible, with the end of the month to ensure that the costs are matched with the corresponding value of the work. It may, however, happen that the valuation is prepared well before or after the end of the accounting period, for example to maximise returns where fluctuations are recovered under the formula method. In such circumstances it will be necessary to adjust the valuation by an addition or subtraction of the value of the work carried out before or after the end of the accounting period. Frequently the builder's surveyor will calculate this adjustment pro rata to the number of working days in excess or short of the close down period. This method of amending the valuation, however, may well be very inaccurate as production on site does not necessarily progress at an even rate. This is of course due to any number of factors such as weather conditions, labour or material delays or erratic production output.

It will therefore be preferable for the builder's surveyor to undertake an accurate assessment of the value of the work completed at the end of the accounting period. This should preferably take the form of a site inspection and a complete revaluation of the work at that point in time. Each aspect of the valuation must be examined, including materials on site at the relevant date. Such procedures are of course time-consuming.

VARIATIONS AND CLAIMS

SSAP9 provides that:

> 'Where approved variations have been made to a contract in the course of it and the amount to be received in respect of these variations has not yet been settled and is likely to be a material factor in the outcome, it is necessary to make a conservative estimate of the amount likely to be received and this is then treated as part of the total sales value. On the other hand, provision needs to be made for foreseen claims or penalties payable arising out of delays in completion or from other causes.'

It is unfortunately an all-too-frequent occurrence for variations to be substantially undervalued or omitted from the appropriate valuation.

The correct payment for the work when remeasured and valued by the client's quantity surveyor and builder's surveyor may well be included in later valuations or in the final account.

It is therefore in order to add a conservative estimate of the value of official variations to the appropriate internal valuation. It is important to note that such estimates must be a conservative and not an *optimistic* valuation. Where variations have not been agreed by the architect or client they must be regarded as claims.

SSAP9 provides that:

> 'The settlement of claims arising from circumstances not envisaged in the contract or arising as an indirect consequence of approved variations is subject to a high level of uncertainty relating to the outcome of future negotiations. In view of this, it is generally prudent to make provision for receipts in respect of such claims only when negotiations have reached an advanced stage and there is evidence in writing of the acceptability of the claim in principle to the purchaser, an indication of the magnitude of the sum involved also being available.'

It is clear, therefore, that any costs relating to claims must be set against the internal valuation without any adjustment or provision for possible future payments. It may also arise that claims or contra-charges may exist between the main contractor and sub-contractors and similar rules of prudence should also be applied.

ACCURACY OF ADJUSTMENTS

It will be apparent that a meaningful and accurate adjustment to costs and an accurate assessment of the internal valuation will be dependent upon certain factors:

(a) The ability and diligence of the builder's surveyor.
(b) The knowledge of both the builder's surveyor and management of any adjustment made to the bill of quantities at tender stage, such as front-end loading and weighting of individual items.
(c) The capacity for smaller builders to be able to allocate sufficient resources to achieve the degree of accuracy that is desirable or indeed required by the provisions of SSAP9.

Contract No	Contract Name	Date	Date Contract Commenced
			Extension of Time
Contract Sum	Estimated Final Account	Contract Period	Completion Due

Valuation

External Valuation No   Date of Valuation

Gross Valuation

Adjustments	Deduct	Add
Preliminaries		
Measured work		
Materials on site		
Nominated subcontractors		
Provisional work		
Variations		
Fluctuations		
Weighting		
Any other		
Totals		

Internal Valuation

Adjustment for work carried out before or after close of accounting period

Deduct – Cost to date.

Gross margin – profit/loss

Less unallocated overheads

Net Margin – profit/loss

Cost

Accounting Period

Ending ————

	Book Cost	Adjust- ments	Adjusted Cost
Direct Labour			
Labour only Subcontractors			
Labour & Material Subcontractors			
Nominated Subcontractors			
Nominated Suppliers			
Materials			
Hired Plant			
Own Plant			
Special Expenses			
Total Cost			

Provisions/Foreseeable Losses		Potential Credits	
Remedial work		Claims	
Defects liability		Variations	
Unprofitable future work		Any other	
Winter working			
Increased costs – not recoverable			
Any other			
Total		Total	

Fig. 11.1 Cost value reconciliation statement

COST VALUE RECONCILIATION

Once the builder is reasonably certain that both the internal valuation and the adjusted cost accurately reflect the financial position of a project at a given date, a comparison of the two figures will reveal the estimated gross profit on the project at that point in time.

The majority of builders enter the respective costs and adjustments and details of both the external and internal valuations on a standard company cost value reconciliation/cost value comparison format. In addition to this basic information it is common practice also to include other details relating to the contract or development such as cash received, outstanding retention, claims pending, contract sum, contract period, extension of time, etc. A typical cost value reconciliation format is shown in Fig. 11.1.

The information produced is obviously of a highly sensitive nature and it is customary for the majority of companies to restrict circulation of the completed format to senior key management personnel only. Frequently, builders assemble the information necessary to prepare the cost value reconciliation on as many as a dozen separate forms or financial reports. Only the chief surveyor, contract manager or accountant assemble the financial information to produce the monthly gross profit or loss figures.

OVERHEADS

In Chapter 3 the relationship between overheads, profitability and turnover was discussed in detail and the effect of changes in turnover on profit margins was identified. The key issue in any realistic assessment of actual profit or loss is the method adopted by the company to allocate overheads to individual projects. In fact many companies ignore overheads and leave their inclusion till the end of the company's financial year.

SSAP9 lays down specific guidelines regarding the costing of overheads. Production overheads, together with other overheads if any, arising in bringing the product or service to its present location and condition should be included in the cost.

Production overheads are defined in SSAP9 as:

'overheads incurred in respect of materials, labour or services for production, based on the normal level of activity, taking one year with another. For this purpose each overhead should be classified according to function (e.g. production, selling or administration) so as to ensure the inclusion in cost of conversion of those overheads (including depreciation) which relate to production, notwithstanding that these may accrue wholly or partly on a time basis.'

When contracts are awarded or development projects authorised to commence by management, overheads relating to design and any marketing or selling costs incurred prior to commencement of the project may be included in arriving at costs. The allocation of overheads must usually involve the exercise of personal judgement, particularly in the classification of overheads by the function of production, marketing, selling or administration. This is particularly the case in smaller companies, where management is involved in several or all of the functions on a daily basis.

The costs relating to general management, as distinct from functional management outlined above, are not directly related to current production. As a consequence they are therefore excluded from the cost of conversion and consequently from the cost of work in progress.

Problems may also arise in allocating the costs of central service departments such as the accounts department. The cost of the department may be divided between:

(a) Production – by paying production direct and indirect wages and salaries, by controlling purchases and by preparing periodic accounts for the production units.
(b) Marketing and distribution – by analysing sales and by controlling the sales ledger.
(c) General administration – by preparing management and annual accounts and budgets, by controlling cash resources and by planning investments.

Only those costs of the accounts department that can be reasonably allocated to the production should be included in the cost of work in progress.

COSTING METHODS

Normally site overheads such as site telephone, electricity, rates and site staff are charged directly to the contract, as discussed in Chapter 9. It is also possible that surveying and management staff, if site based, will also be charged directly to the project. All other overheads fall into the classification of chargeable or unchargeable to work in progress as discussed above, and will be treated as such in the cost and financial accounts.

INTERNAL MANAGEMENT ACCOUNTS

In the preparation of internal management accounts the distinction between chargeable and unchargeable overheads may be ignored in order that the net profit on individual contracts or developments may be identified at cost value reconciliation each month.

To achieve this objective the actual cost of all uncosted overheads may be spread over the projects currently under construction by a variety of methods:

(a) Pro rata to the total cost of work carried out during the accounting period on each project. For example, if the monthly costs of projects A, B and C were £10000, £6000 and £4000 at the end of the accounting period, overheads of £2000 would be allocated as £1000, £600 and £400 respectively.

(b) Pro rata to the total labour cost arising during the accounting period on each project. The management justification for this alternative method is the assumption that the majority of overheads are more directly related to labour than to other costs.

(c) By accurate calculation. Salaried overheads are calculated on the basis of time sheets prepared by each member of staff or individual departments in the builder's office; for example, surveying, planning and buying may charge out costs to projects on the basis of an agreed formula. Any residual costs not so allocated, or costs relating to abortive work, will be charged to a special account. Other general overheads will be costed on the basis of the actual use of the resource concerned. This method will of course be time-consuming.

(d) The detailed overhead budget (see Chapter 3) may be used as the basis for allocating overheads. Within the breakdown the calculated overhead figures are allocated to individual projects using method (a) or (b) or (c) above. The actual overhead cost will be monitored against the budget and adjustments made at periodic intervals, probably three-monthly.

An alternative approach, adopted by some companies, is to apply a standard percentage surcharge of, say, 10% to the total project costs each month to cover overheads and administrative charges. As a result, the net profit shown by cost value reconciliation may vary substantially from the true profit figure. Such a system, however, does have the advantage of restricting knowledge of the true profit to a few members of senior staff.

TURNOVER

SSAP9 states that:

> 'the allocation of overheads included in the valuation of stocks and work in progress needs to be based on the company's normal level of activity, taking one year with another. The governing factor is that the cost of unused capacity should be written off in the current year. In determining what constitutes 'normal' the following factors need to be considered:
>
> (a) The volume of production which the production facilities are intended by their designers and by management to produce under the working conditions (e.g. single or double shift) prevailing during the year.
> (b) The budgeted level of activity for the year under review and for the ensuing year.
> (c) The level of activity achieved both in the year under review and in previous years.
>
> Although temporary changes in the load of activity may be ignored, persistent variation should lead to a revision of the previous "norm".'

These considerations are of course most important when considering the dramatic fluctuations in turnover which arise in building companies. The principle to be adopted, therefore, is geared to a realistic assessment not only of overheads during the year but also of the corresponding projected turnover. Fluctuations of up to, say, 15% of the budgeted turnover could be ignored, but any reduction in turnover in excess of this figure must be reflected in the cost of the unused capacity being written off in the current year and not charged to work in progress.

CONCLUSION

SSAP9 states that:

> 'the adoption of a conservative approach to the valuation of stocks and work in progress has sometimes been used as one of the reasons for omitting selected production overheads. In so far as the circumstances of the business require an element of prudence in determining the amount at which stocks and work in progress are stated, this needs to be taken into account in the determination of net realisable value and not by the exclusion from costs of selected overheads.'

In effect, therefore, management is faced with a number of decisions:

(a) The decision as to which overheads are site overheads and which are company overheads. The site overheads will normally be directly related to items in the preliminaries section of the bill of quantities and costed via the cost accounts.
(b) The decision as to what proportion of company overheads may be correctly classified as production overheads and therefore included with the cost of work in progress.
(c) The method of allocation of all overheads to the activities of the company to achieve a true calculation of profit or loss margins on work in progress in the management accounts.

Usually only site overheads will be included in the cost accounts; other overheads will be shown in the financial accounts or as adjustments in the management accounts.

VISUAL PRESENTATION

It is a useful management tool to maintain a graph or histogram of the margin calculated by the cost value reconciliation process each month. The margin should be entered on the graph monthly, concluding with the actual profit or loss at final account stage. This visual presentation will indicate the efficiency of the surveying and management staff in accurately calculating and completing the cost value reconciliation format. Errors in any individual monthly cost value reconciliation can usually be easily identified by a blip in the graph, although obviously, from time to time, actual events on site may be identified as the cause. Equally, any dramatic upward movement of the margin at final account stage will usually indicate under-recovery of cost by the builder's surveying staff during the progress of the work.

MANIPULATION OF FIGURES

There may well be a temptation for surveying or management staff to manipulate input figures where an unusual or unexpected margin is calculated at the monthly cost value reconciliation. The use of various members of staff or separate departments to provide the input, which is only subsequently collated at senior management level, will reduce the opportunity for such tampering. Unfortunately, however, it is all too easy in many companies for the input to the valuation, adjusted cost and overheads allocation to be manipulated, either to conceal an apparent loss in the hope that circumstances will improve in future months or to understate the profit to create a hidden reserve against possible future setbacks. This manipulation may arise at both junior and senior levels in the management structure of the company or even at board level. Moreover, each may be unaware that other departments in the company have tampered with the figures.

A study of the results of several years' cost value reconciliation records will however give the directors/accountants/auditors some measure of confidence (or lack of it) in the surveying records of the company.

AUDIT

The cost value reconciliation process is a crucial and integral constituent in the calculation of the amount included in a company's financial accounts for value of work in progress.

The average accountant during the audit process is often heavily dependent on the ability of the contractor's surveyor to provide accurate and correct financial information. Many, if not the majority, of the adjustments to both the cost accounts and quantity surveyor's valuation are outside the accountant's professional expertise. In addition, within a short period, because of the progress of work on a construction site it is virtually impossible for anyone to check the accuracy of any particular valuation.

Many auditors will only start the audit process weeks, or even months, after the end of a company's financial year. For any meaningful independent assessment of the valuation of work in progress it is essential for the auditor or his representative to visit each site at the end of the financial year. At this site visit the stage reached in the work should be noted or a photograph taken and some assessment made of the approximate value of the work completed at that time. The accountant will thus be able to verify independently, as far as he is able, the accuracy of the valuation. Many auditors of construction companies have developed a rudimentary expertise by adopting such an independent check. In certain circumstances some auditors may wish to employ their own surveying staff.

COST VALUE RECONCILIATION FOR DEVELOPMENT PROJECTS

The principal difference between a normal cost value reconciliation and one for a project without external bills of quantities is that the valuation will be prepared internally and not verified by the client's independent quantity surveyor.

Where there is an internal bill of quantities or estimate the valuation is perhaps best based on the estimated cost excluding both profit and overheads. The cost value reconciliation process will then measure the production performance and efficiency and reveal any additional profit or loss against cost. The estimated profit and sale price will be identified in the feasibility study (see Chapter 7).

The sale price (or prices when more than one unit is involved) will be separately monitored against the feasibility study in order to calculate any adjustment to the projected profit on a project. The result of the cost value reconciliation process will then be added to or deducted from this estimated profit to reveal the revised estimated profit or loss for the whole project each month.

The adjustments made to both the valuation and the cost will be similar to those described for contracting. Obviously, where projects are internally funded, front-end loading and other forms of weighting will not be applicable.

Monthly valuations can be arranged internally to coincide with the close down of the financial and cost accounts. It is of course important for the builder's surveyor to take much greater care with the preparation of the valuation, as the discipline of the monitoring role of the client's quantity surveyor will be lacking.

In small companies when there is no estimate it may be necessary to produce an approximate estimate or breakdown of the constituent elements of the sale price in order that the valuation can be prepared. For example, for an individual house: land, legal and estate agent's fees, construction costs, selling and marketing costs, overheads and profit.

12 Valuation of work in progress in company accounts

INTRODUCTION

When considering the accounts of construction companies, work in progress is an extremely grey area; builders, by legitimate manipulation of attributable profit, foreseeable losses, reserves and provisions, can create a policy regarding profit taking which will (within limits) control the declared profits of a company in any particular year.

It may be difficult to distinguish between those companies which have adopted a prudent and conservative approach to accounting policies and those who have rashly anticipated the outcome of building projects and over-declared the profit. Moreover, if a construction company is taken over or bought out, the valuation of work in progress is crucially important. The company's policy regarding the valuation of stock, land stock and work in progress must be clearly identified and adjusted if necessary to prudent accounting practice.

SSAP9

SSAP9 in the opening paragraph highlights the problem with work in progress in that:

> 'No area of accounting has produced wider differences in practice than the computation of the amount at which stocks and work in progress are stated in financial accounts.'

In order to resolve this problem, SSAP9 seeks to define the practices, to narrow the differences and variations in those practices, and to ensure adequate disclosure in the accounts.

The Exposure Draft ED40, issued by the Accounting Standards Committee in November 1986, when adopted, will change the balance sheet presentation of work in progress, but there will be no effect on the profit and loss account because any attributable profit and foreseeable losses will be measured in the same way as under the existing standard.

In the notes on their annual accounts defining accounting definitions and policies, companies might include the following typical statements.

'Profit for the year

The profit for the year includes the result of the year's operations on contracts based on directors' valuations of work in progress, together with balances in respect of work done in prior years. No credit is taken for claims until the cash is received.'

'Work in progress

Work in progress is valued at the lower of cost and net realisable value. Long-term contract work in progress is valued at cost plus attributable profit less foreseeable losses and contingencies. Progress payments received and receivable are deducted in arriving at the balance sheet figure.'

WORK IN PROGRESS

In the construction industry the majority of building projects have contract periods of many months, and in some cases several years. At the end of a building company's financial year, therefore, the work in progress may well include projects that have just started, are in progress, or are virtually complete. In addition the majority of companies adopt the policy of contracts or development remaining in work in progress until the final payment is received. Such a policy will therefore result in contracts remaining in work in progress until the final acount has been prepared by the client's quantity surveyor, approved by the client and contractor, and the final certificate issued and paid by the architect. Thus projects will remain in work in progress not only for the time of the defects liability period of six months, but possibly for several years after completion.

Once the final payment has been made the contract or development must be taken out of work in progress and the total profit or, where attributable profit has already been taken, the residual profit, included in the accounts for the current financial year.

SSAP9 does draw a distinction between work in progress and long-term work in progress, long-term work in progress being defined as contracts where the contract period will extend for a period exceeding one year.

SHORT-TERM CONTRACT WORK IN PROGRESS

SSAP9 requires that the amount at which work in progress, other than long-term contract work in progress, is stated in periodic financial statements should be the total of the lower of cost and net realisable value of the separate items of work in progress.

It is important to note that no reference is made to profit and therefore in the case of short-term contracts (contracts lasting less than one year) profit need only be brought into the accounts when the final payment is made, possibly several years after completion of the work. Some companies, therefore, in their notes to the accounts, amend the requirements of SSAP9 by stating that: 'no distinction is drawn between long-term and short-term contracts'. This amendment will therefore enable the company to include attributable profit on work in progress for short-term contracts.

It will be helpful to examine what is included in costs and what is meant by realisable value.

Valuation at cost

Cost is, defined in SSAP9 as being 'that expenditure which has been incurred in the normal course of business in bringing the product or service to its present location and condition', and should include:

(a) Cost of purchase, including import duties, transport and handling costs and any other directly attributable costs, less any trade discount, rebate or subsidies.

(b) Cost of conversion, including direct labour, direct expenses and sub-contract work, together with production overheads and other overheads associated with bringing the product to its present location and condition.

In practice the majority of construction costs can be clearly identified within the SSAP9 definition, but the treatment of overheads will require careful consideration (see Chapters 9 and 11). It is important to appreciate that the costs would include waste, errors, and any excessive charges for labour, plant or materials.

Where a builder fails to maintain an adequate costing system, other methods of calculating costs will have to be utilised. One method of arriving at cost is the use of selling price or final account less an estimated profit margin. This is only acceptable if it can be demonstrated that the method gives a reasonable approximation of the actual cost.

In view of the obvious inaccuracies and difficulties with such calculations it is essential that accurate costing records are maintained to ensure that the valuation at cost is a meaningful record of the company's financial position.

Valuation at net realisable value

The concept of valuation at net realisable value is discussed in Chapter 10. The principal reasons why net realisable value is likely to be less than cost are:

(a) There has been an increase in costs due, for example, to inflation, and all or part of the total increase is not recoverable under the terms of the contract or sale agreement.

(b) A fall in selling price. This might apply on a contract, if the client imposes the clause relating to liquidated damages, or more commonly in the case of speculative development where prices fall following a downturn in the economy and a deterioration in market conditions.

(c) Physical deterioration of stocks. This will be most likely to occur where materials are stored on site but could equally apply to completed unsold residential, industrial or commercial properties.

(d) Obsolescence of products. This may arise in speculative residential, industrial or commercial development where competitors more precisely judge market trends and client demand.

(e) Market strategy to sell at a loss. The builder, as part of his marketing strategy, may decide to tender at a figure below cost in order to maintain turnover, contribute to overheads, or gain experience in a new range of work or a foothold with a new client with the hope of a follow on of profitable contracts. In the case of speculative development the builder may decide to sell at a loss simply to maintain cash flow.

(f) Errors in production or purchasing. In the construction industry losses arising during the purchasing process (discussed in Chapter 5) and due to weather, poor standards or workmanship or weak site management, are legion. In addition, pricing errors may occur at tender stage and in contract work the builder's surveyor may neglect to identify and claim for variations arising during the progress of the work.

Where companies are involved with speculative development it is possible that excess stocks of completed housing, industrial or commercial properties may build up. The impending delay in the realisation of the sales receipts will increase the risk that the circumstances outlined in (a) to (e) above will occur and will therefore need to be taken into account when assessing net realisable value.

Short-term contract work in progress is valued at the lower of cost or net realisable value. In effect therefore, the main aim in this assessment is to determine for each contract or development the probability, or reasonable certainty, that the final margin on the project is to be a profit or loss. The cost value reconciliation process will, therefore, be an essential ingredient in arriving at this decision.

Each project will be valued at the lower of:

(a) Cost: where the cost value reconciliation shows a profitable position at the end of the financial year and it is considered that this profit will be maintained until the end of the defects liability period.
(b) Net realisable value: cost less known losses and provision for further foreseeable losses, including maintenance and provision for remedial work arising during the defects liability period.

The work in progress figure stated in the accounts will of course be the total for all the contracts and development of the company.

One further factor in the calculation of cost for the valuation of work in progress is the decision as to which items of overheads are written off in the year in which they arise, and which are included in the cost of conversion. This decision will obviously have the effect of transferring profit from one financial year to the next. The company should, however, be consistent in the policy which it applies.

In addition, where the cost includes internal plant hire charges and the plant department is profitable, some profit could be included in the valuation of work in progress in the accounts. Some companies, therefore, make a note in their accounts to this effect.

LONG-TERM CONTRACT WORK IN PROGRESS

Where the contract period for a project exceeds one year, SSAP9 requires that separate consideration should be given to the valuation of the work in progress. If the taking of profit was deferred until the completion of such contracts the profit and loss account would only reflect the results of contracts which have been completed, or the final account settled, by the end of the financial year, rather than a fair view of the activities of the company during the year.

SSAP9 states that it is therefore appropriate to take credit for ascertainable profit while contracts are in progress, subject to certain limitations. Where it is expected there will be a loss on a contract as a whole, provision needs to be made, in accordance with the 'prudence concept' for the whole of the loss as soon as it is recognised. This has the effect of reducing the value of the work done to date to its net realisable value. Hence the gross amount at which long-term contract work in progress should be stated in the accounts is at cost plus attributable profits (if any) less foreseeable losses (if any).

The comments made earlier in this chapter concerning contracts remaining in work in progress until final payment is received apply equally to long-term contract work in progress.

In view of the complexity of ascertaining both attributable profit and foreseeable losses, it is appropriate to give detailed consideration to these concepts.

Attributable profit

Attributable profit is defined in SSAP9 as:

'that part of the total profit currently estimated to arise over the duration of the contract(after allowing for likely increases in costs so far as not recoverable under the terms of the contract) which fairly reflects the profit attributable to that part of the work performed at the accounting date. There can be no attributable profit until the outcome of the contract can be assessed with reasonable certainty.'

Any profit that is included in the valuation of work in progress must not only reflect the proportion of the work carried out at the accounting date, but also take into account inequalities of profitability in various stages of a contract, estimated future cost of rectification and cost expected to arise during the defects liability period. These inequalities of profitability may result from a number of factors, including increased costs where not recoverable under the terms of the contract, weighting of the priced bills, and estimating errors.

Where the outcome of a contract can be assessed with reasonable certainty before the completion date then attributable profit should be taken up provided that:

(a) Of the profit which in the light of all the circumstances can be foreseen with a reasonable degree of certainty to arise on completion of the contract, there should only be regarded as earned to date that part which prudently reflects the amount of work performed to date.

(b) The judgement involved is exercised with prudence.

(c) The method used for taking up of profits is consistently applied.

Where the outcome of a contract cannot reasonably be assessed before the completion of the contract or indeed the final account, then in such cases it is not prudent to take up 'any profit'. This is particularly the case when the estimated profit on a contract arises largely from claims or variations not approved by the client. Claims and variations were discussed in Chapter 11, but it must be emphasised that it is generally prudent only to include the value of such claims in work in progress when negotiations have reached an advanced stage and there is evidence in writing from the client, or his representative, of the acceptability of the claim.

It is therefore important that whatever methods are adopted by a builder for calculating attributable profit they must be consistently applied to all the projects of the company and from one year to the next.

The estimated final profit of a contract which extends over several years will inevitably vary in each accounting year in the light of the prevailing circumstances. The profit taken each year, less profit already taken in earlier years, may not therefore necessarily represent the proportion of the total profit on the contract which is appropriate to the amount of work carried out in the accounting period.

In the case of large development schemes, where the ultimate selling prices of individual units are uncertain, it will be logical to divide the project into phases for both cost and valuation purposes. This will enable the profit of each phase to be separately calculated and isolated from the profit or loss in other phases, thus reducing the level of uncertainty on the outcome of the project as a whole. It is of course essential that costing between phases is accurately and correctly maintained and verified by the audit process.

Company policy regarding attributable profit

SSAP9, when referring to the taking up of attributable profit, continually uses such expressions as 'outcome of the contract can be reasonably foreseen', 'reasonable certainty', 'judgement should be exercised with prudence', 'prudently reflects' and 'in accordance with the prudence concept'.

In the construction industry many companies consider that profits can only be treated as secure, or reasonably certain, at the end of the defects liability period, when the final account has been agreed, the final certificate issued by the architect and all monies received from the client; equally, when considering residential or commercial development projects, when the last unit is sold or let and the initial NHBC guarantee period or defects liability period has expired. The author has more than once been involved with a project where a substantial proportion of the profit on a contract has been absorbed by problems arising in the defects liability period.

It will be apparent that the interpretation of 'reasonable certainty', 'prudent', etc., will vary from company to company. Many companies will be reluctant to take any profit on long-term work in progress and endeavour to operate a very conservative policy. Profit will only be taken up on practical completion of the project or even at final account stage. Other companies, on the other hand, may take up as much profit as possible on work in progress, with the associated problems of losses accruing in later years.

A 'prudent' policy, bearing in mind the uncertainties of the construction process, might be to adopt a moderately conservative approach by taking up and including in the valuation of work in progress between 25% and 50% of the calculated profit. This policy must of course be subject to the company having a proven and reliable cost value reconciliation procedure. When attributable profit is taken up and included in work in progress it will be apparent that the cost value reconciliation process is a crucial tool in determining profit to date on contracts and development. Accurate cost value reconciliation is essential if any meaningful assessment of contract or development profitability is to be achieved in accordance with the guidelines laid down in SSAP9.

It will also be necessary to examine both surveying and cost records to ensure that all payments to suppliers and sub-contractors have been finalised and all invoices received and costed. In practice only the larger provincial and national construction and development companies have the expertise and personnel to fully meet the requirements laid down in SSAP9.

Foreseeable losses

Foreseeable losses are defined in SSAP9 as

'losses which are currently estimated to arise over the duration of the contract (after allowing for estimated remedial and maintenance costs, and increases in costs so far as not recoverable under the terms of the contract). This estimate is required irrespective of:

(a) Whether or not work has yet commenced on such contracts;
(b) The proportion of work carried out at the accounting date;
(c) The amount of profits expected to arise on other contracts.'

When it is expected that a loss will arise on a contract a prudent provision will need to be made for the whole of the loss as soon as it is recognised. This action will in effect reduce the value of work done to date to its net realisable value.

Where unprofitable contracts represent a substantial proportion of a company's turnover, the related administrative overheads to be incurred during the period to the completion of those contracts should also be included in the calculation of the provision for losses.

Future losses will be a sensitive area for the majority of builders and will entail careful examination of all the relevant data. They will be highlighted by:

(a) The monthly cost value reconciliation revealing a pattern of loss.
(b) Anticipated lower output due, for example, to winter working, adverse weather conditions, labour or material shortages and site conditions.
(c) Known unprofitable future work. The builder's surveyor should be able to identify future losses by analysis of cost targets for labour, materials and sub-contract work against the relative tender rates in the bill of quantities or other estimate.
(d) Delays in the contract which may lead to extensions of time with associated increased cost, particularly preliminary items. There is of course also the possibility of liquidated damages being applied.
(e) Remedial work – making good any defects and damage that may occur before the works are handed over to the client. In addition, there may be unrecoverable costs associated with cleaning and clearing the site at completion.
(f) Defects liability period. The majority of building contracts include a requirement for the builder to make good any defects in materials or workmanship which become apparent after the building has been handed over. The defects liability period for the majority of contracts is usually stated as 6 months. Following satisfactory completion of the work by the builder a final certificate will be issued and any outstanding monies, including retention, will be released. In the case of private housing development constructed under the terms of an

NHBC agreement, the builder is liable to remedy defects in certain items such as the heating and electrical installation for a period of 12 months and the structure and finishes for a period of 2 years. An insurance policy then applies to the structure only for a period of from 2 to 10 years. Retention is rarely held by clients or their solicitors for any latent defects which may arise on residential development, although retention may well be held for any remedial work outstanding at the date of legal completion. It would be usual for provisions to be made for some of the above items such as remedial work based on the builder's experience of similar work undertaken under similar circumstances by the use of an appropriate percentage.

In general the majority of builders will experience some difficulty in meeting the requirements of SSAP9 regarding foreseeable losses. To a large extent, reasonably accurate assessment of foreseeable losses is dependent on the intimate knowledge of each contract or development by the respective surveyor and management. In addition they will need the facilities to ensure that accurate comparisons are made between the tender rates or estimate and the cost target for each section and every aspect of the work. Many smaller companies do not have the staff or financial resources to produce such accurate information and will rely on approximate figures only.

Company policy regarding foreseeable losses

The comments made earlier in this chapter regarding attributable profit apply equally to foreseeable losses. The builder is obliged to make prudent provision as soon as a loss is recognised. The conservative and very prudent builder will tend to make excessive provisions for possible future losses, thus, in effect, creating a contingency reserve. On the other hand, a rash or incompetent builder may overlook future losses either by accident or as a deliberate policy.

The auditor is of course almost entirely in the hands of the builder as he is extremely unlikely to have the time or necessary expertise to identify the majority of foreseeable losses. He may, however, be in a position to examine the methods adopted by the surveyor or management. Moreover, he will of course be able to examine provisions made year on year and draw an independent conclusion.

EXPOSURE DRAFT 40

The preface to the exposure draft sets out the background which gave rise to the necessity for changes to the original SSAP9 to take place and the effects on the presentation of company accounts in that:

'This proposed revision to SSAP9 is issued primarily to provide an integrated financial statement presentation of long-term contracting activity which accords with international practice. The proposals will have the further advantage of removing the present conflict between SSAP9 and Schedule 4 to the Companies Act 1985, Schedule 4 to the Companies (Northern Ireland) Order 1986 and (in the Republic of Ireland) the Schedule to the Companies (Amendment) Act 1986, in regard to the balance sheet carrying value of long-term contracts.

The present SSAP9 practice is to state long-term contracts in the balance sheet at cost plus any attributable profit, less any foreseeable losses and progress payments received and receivable. The conflict referred to above arises in respect of the element of attributable profit because paragraph 22 of Schedule 4 to both the Companies Act 1986 and the Companies (Northern Ireland) Order 1986 and paragraph 10 of the Schedule to the Companies (Amendment) Act 1986 provide that current assets shall be stated at purchase price or production cost (or net realisable value if lower).

The method of accounting for long-term contracts specified in SSAP9 requires that attributable profits (if any) should be recognised in the profit and loss account and added to the cumulative cost of long-term contracts in the balance sheet. SSAP9 does not presently address how contract turnover and related costs should be recorded in the profit and loss account. In practice, a variety of methods have been used to determine the turnover disclosed in each accounting period. However, in many cases, this has not been derived from a formal integration of turnover, cost and balance sheet accounting. The balance sheet presentation of long-term contracts has continued to reflect, on a contract-by-contract basis, cumulative volumes of costs incurred and attributable profits, less payments on account, with eventual elimination of the components relating to a particular contract at the time when the contract is determined to have been completed.

Although it is proposed to change this method of accounting, paragraph 15 of the exposure draft states that in some circumstances disclosure of cumulative costs and payments on account in respect of all uncompleted contracts may be regarded as useful information. The ASC would be particularly interested to know what use is made of such disclosures and whether the disclosures should be recommended or required.

The proposed revision to SSAP9 specifies a balance sheet presentation which takes account of amounts which have been transferred to the profit and loss account. There will be no effect on the profit and loss account because any attributable profit and foreseeable losses will be measured in the same way as under the existing standard. Opinion is divided on whether future losses (in excess of balances of cost remaining after transfers to cost of sales) should be classified as provisions or accruals.

An effect of the proposals is that the profit and loss account and balance sheet are fully integrated. This is not the case with the existing SSAP9.

The opportunity has also been taken to revise the definition of a long-term contract.'

It will be apparent that the builder will retain every opportunity for 'creative accounting' in that foreseeable losses, attributable profit and the allocation of overheads can be adjusted, within defined limits, to provide for profit, loss or the creation of reserves at the discretion of the directors. This may of course be with the knowledge and approval of the auditors or at worst entirely hidden within the surveying records of the company with, or indeed without, the knowledge of the directors.

INDEX